Prompt One

Five short modern plays

Prompts One, *Two* and *Three* form a new series for schools, bringing together short, contemporary plays eminently to be enjoyed in a variety of ways. Many of them have been written with young people in mind, and some, where necessary, have been adapted to facilitate their use in a school context. The volumes are graded in difficulty.

Following on from the popular *Playbill* series, *Prompts* are collections which truly represent some of the best of recent contemporary theatre and television drama.

PROMPT TWO

Speech Day (Barry Hines); *The Ballad of Ben Bagot* (Peter Terson); *Here is Your Life* (Bob Taylor); *Burglars* (David Rudkin); *A Question of Honour* (Don Shaw).

PROMPT THREE

They Don't All Open Men's Boutiques (Willis Hall); *Decibels* (John Hale); *Bovver* (Roy Minton); *Old Comrades* (Robert Holles); *The Punishment* (E. A. Whitehead).

Other drama anthologies edited by Alan Durband:

Playbill One
Playbill Two
Playbill Three
Second Playbill One
Second Playbill Two
Second Playbill Three
New Directions

Prompt One

Five short modern plays

Edited by Alan Durband

HUTCHINSON OF LONDON

Hutchinson & Co (Publishers) Ltd
3 Fitzroy Square, London W1

London Melbourne Sydney Auckland
Wellington Johannesburg and agencies
throughout the world

First published 1976
Third impression 1978

Set in Monotype Fournier
Printed in Great Britain by litho at The Anchor Press Ltd
and bound by Wm Brendon & Son Ltd, both of
Tiptree, Essex

ISBN 0 09 125981 9

Contents

Introduction

Prompt One contains plays by Alan England, Cecil P. Taylor, Trevor Harvey, Michael Barwis, and C. G. Bond.

1 *The Plays*

Alan England's *A Day in the Mind of Tich Oldfield* is an imaginative romp based on the adventures of a boy with a fertile mind. His action-packed day begins with a T.V. session in which he scoops the million-pound first prize with his gift of mimicry. But later on, in school, his luck changes. His impression of 'Jammy' Chivers earns him a hundred lines, the first of several setbacks in a day full of ups and downs. Tich may be small in stature, but in heroic endeavour he's a giant. Political reformer, pilot, Tarzan, and family provider, he takes the buffeting of fortune in his manly stride. He refuses to be daunted – at least in his imagination.

Apples by Cecil P. Taylor is also about illusion and reality. In this allegory, written for a young people's theatre group in Alnwick, Northumberland, a bunch of school-leavers sets out in search of a symbolic apple tree, said by their teachers to be laden with fruit. For some people, there are plenty of apples around, but the kids discover that the path to the tree is a very difficult one. The further along it they go, the more obstacles there seem to be. Eventually, they are side-tracked into a blind alley where they turn handles for a living and settle for bags of chips. Idealism and memories fade. New kids arrive, fresh from the shelter of their school, asking to be guided to the great apple tree. The old kids don't know what they are talking about.

That something is wrong with society is the assumption behind Trevor Harvey's *Voyage of a Lifetime*, a modern Noah story originally written for the Brighton and Hove Spotlight Youth Theatre Group. The ark has been updated – now it's a spaceship – but the essential message is the same and so are many of the characters. In this musical version of the biblical story, bureaucracy frustrates Mr Knower and commercialism deceives and exploits him. Times may have changed, it would seem, but people haven't. Off everyone goes on extended package tours to outer space, leaving the Knower family alone to start all over again; hopefully, to make a better job of things than last time.

What went wrong? Michael Barwis drops some thoughtful hints in *Island*, the scene of which might well be down the road from where you're reading this. There's a war going on out there. The great god Diesel and his Juggernauts are bombarding us with noise, pollution, and physical danger, all for the greater glory of the motorway. This is an amusing piece of fantasy with a disturbing element of truth in it.

Equally disturbing is Chris Bond's *George*, which spotlights another weakness in our social structure. George is a Mynah bird, the sole companion of David's mother in her old age. George can only whistle, and speak what he has learned. In any other context, he'd be cute. But in David and Judy's trendy living room, he's quite out of place. He looks it, and when he opens his beak, he sounds it too. His voice is the voice of an old woman, plaintively complaining about loneliness, poverty and cold. David and Judy listen with horror, their comfortable complacency shattered. Covering the cage with a sheet gives them a short respite, but the worst is yet to come. The truth of their selfish indifference is literally brought home to them.

2 *The Playwrights*

Alan England studied English at Liverpool University, and has taught in three secondary schools and a College of Education. A regular contributor to specialist magazines and journals, he has published several anthologies – *Looking at Scenes* and *Two Ages of Man* (Oliver & Boyd) – and a project kit, *Caves*. He has written many schools programmes for B.B.C. Radio Sheffield; a documentary play, *Maoris, Missionaries and Muskets*; for B.B.C. T.V., two children's plays and a serial; and a series of programmes for B.B.C. *Drama Workshop*. His work has been toured by Nottingham Playhouse Company and the Sheffield Crucible *Vanguard* team. His present post is Lecturer in Drama in the University of Sheffield Department of Education.

Cecil P. Taylor was born in Glasgow in 1929. He left school at fourteen, tried his hand at a number of jobs, began writing poetry, then short stories, and finally plays. He has been described as 'perhaps the most gifted of the young Scottish dramatists working with the Traverse Theatre in Edinburgh'. He has written many television plays, including some for schools, a film script, and a number of full-length stage plays: *The Rise and Fall of Joe Soap, Happy Days are Here Again, Allergy,*

Bread and Butter, *Columba*, and *The Black and White Minstrels*. He is Literary Associate of the Tyneside Theatre Company, and Literary Adviser to the Northumberland Association of Youth Theatres. *Apples* has been staged throughout the country on a tour which concluded with a performance on the sands of Whitley Bay.

Trevor Harvey was born in London in 1944. He trained as a teacher at Brighton College of Education, taught for several years at a primary school, and then took a degree at Sussex University. He was co-founder of the Spotlight Youth Theatre Group, for whom *Voyage of a Lifetime* was written, and with Anthony Foster wrote *Jonah and the Whale* (Oxford University Press). He has written scripts, libretti and stories for children's programmes on B.B.C. Radio Brighton. At present he is lecturer in English at Brighton College of Education.

Michael Barwis is the pen-name of John Adams, a teacher of English at Sevenoaks School, and his father-in-law Clifford Frost, a dental surgeon from Suffolk. This unusual collaboration has existed for some years now, with a winning entry in a B.B.C. radio competition – *Hannah Johnson and the Visitation of God* – and two published plays for schools: *Captain Swing* and *Mutiny at the Nore*. Michael Barwis is at present working on a ballad opera of the Children's Crusade.

C. G. Bond was born in 1945. He started as a child actor at the age of eleven, and has since acted, directed, and written plays for a number of theatres. He was resident playwright at the Victoria Theatre, Stoke-on-Trent, in 1970, and later actor and playwright at the Everyman Theatre, Liverpool, for whom he has written *Tarzan's Last Stand, Simple Simon, Sweeney Todd, Downright Hooligan,* and a new version of Wycherley's *The Country Wife. George* was also written for the Everyman, as part of a programme of short plays. Chris Bond is married, with four small children.

Acknowledgements

For permission to publish the plays in this volume, the editor is grateful to the following authors and their agents: Alan England for *A Day in the Mind of Tich Oldfield*; Cecil P. Taylor and Clive Goodwin Associates for *Apples*; Trevor Harvey for *Voyage of a Lifetime*; John Adams and C. B. Frost for *Island*; C. G. Bond for *George*.

A Day in the Mind of Tich Oldfield

Alan England

Cast

GOOEY SMILES
'BARREL' SNIDE
'JAMMY' CHIVERS
PAM
TICH OLDFIELD
FATHER
MOTHER
'THORNY' BRIAR
ALLMAN
MISS FECKLESS
BUS DRIVER
ZOO KEEPER
BIMBO THE APE

Members of Tich's class, who become rioters, soldiers and plane passengers in Tich's mind.

A Day in the Mind of Tich Oldfield

SCENE: Upstage, a boy, 'TICH' OLDFIELD, *asleep in bed. Downstage, to one side, is a huge 'clapometer' looking like a thermometer with an indicator, and by it stands* PAM, *a girl of Tich's age, dressed in a bathing costume. Onto the downstage area, via some steps, dances an ebullient and unctuous compère,* GOOEY SMILES.

SMILES: Thank you, ladies and gentlemen, thank you. This is your host, Gooey Smiles, and you are tuned in to your favourite talent show, *A Million to One*. We now come to the climax of the evening, the moment when *you* decide the fate of the brave and talented boys who have entertained us so wonderfully tonight. The clapometer will be registering your applause and the winner will receive the magnificent sum of one million pounds. As usual, I shall bring back each of the artists in turn to remind you of what they did, and first, if you remember, we had a youngster who wants to be a romantic pop singer, Darrel (known to his friends as 'Barrel') Snide!

[*Enter* BARREL, *a fat lad in a ridiculous outfit. He carries a guitar. His singing is hopelessly out of tune and the chords he strums are absolute guesswork. The actor can make the tune up as he goes along*]

BARREL: [*Singing*]

Every time I look into my mirror,
There's a face I always love to see.
I'm handsome and I'm clever,
I don't think I shall ever
Meet anyone as marvellous as me.

But, Pamelah! Oh, Pame-lah!
Let's both look in the mirror on the wall.
I'm as happy as can be
When you are next to me,
'Cos next to me I love you best of all.

[*As soon as he finishes,* PAM *raises a card on which is written 'BOO', thereby encouraging the audience to do this. The clapometer fails to move. Re-enter* SMILES]

SMILES: And the clapometer has registered nil, ladies and gentlemen, no points at all for Burbling Barrel, the Git with the Guitar. Never mind, Barrel, the competition is not over yet. Not by a long chalk. And speaking of chalk, we come to our next performer, ladies and gentlemen, and he was, if you recall, the tedious teacher from Oxford – or was it Cambridge? And here he is to offer you a date with boredom – 'Jammy' Chivers!

[*Exit* SMILES *and enter* CHIVERS. *He speaks with his teeth together and draws out his vowels. Horn-rimmed specs perch on the end of his nose*]

CHIVERS: Enthralling events in History. In 55 B.C., Julius Caesar landed, followed closely by Hengist and Horsa in 499 A.D. William the Conqueror landed in 1066 and the Magna Carta was signed in 1215. Simon de Montfort died in 1265 and in 1399 the Peasants revolted . . .

[*As though on cue,* PAM *raises a card marked 'SNORE' and the audience complies.* CHIVERS *carries on, blissfully ignorant*]

Charles the First was executed in 1649, and the monarchy was restored in 1660. In 1788 George the Third went mad and in 1881 there was trouble with the Boers . . .

[*He pronounces it 'Boo-ers' and at this* PAM *raises the card marked 'BOO'. The audience responds limply.* SMILES *returns as* CHIVERS *steps to one side*]

SMILES: Thank you, 'Jammy' Chivers, for that exhaustive, or should I say exhausting, list. And once again, ladies and gentlemen, the clapometer has registered a score of nil. No claps at all for Jammy the Jaw, and so far we have a dead heat – and I do mean dead. I think after that we could all do with a laugh, don't you? And who better to provide it than the mini-mimic from Yorkshire, the little lad with the great big talent, last but by no means least, David ('Tich') Oldfield!

[TICH *has risen from his bed, and he now comes downstage in his pyjamas.* SMILES *makes way for him.* TICH *embarks on a series of 'impressions' of famous people. They can be any that the actor is capable of attempting. After each one, there is laughter or sounds of appreciation. When he finishes,* PAM *raises a card marked 'CLAP' and there is volcanic applause. The indicator on the clapometer rockets to the top and shoots off into the air*]

SMILES: [*Returning*] And we have a winner, ladies and gentlemen, and he has broken both the record and the clapometer. By your applause tonight, you have chosen the person you think should win the jackpot prize of one million pounds. And he is, of course, that inimitable imitator from the North, your friend and my friend, Tich Oldfield.

[*Solemn, regal music as* TICH *comes forward to shake hands with* SMILES *and receive his money*]

SMILES: Congratulations, Tich, and here is your cheque for one million pounds. Don't drop it, will you, it might bounce. Haw! Haw! Haw! Seriously, though, what does it feel like to be rich, Tich? [*He smirks*]

TICH: [*Also smirking*] Absolutely great, mate!

SMILES: [*To audience*] Did you hear that? A natural wit as well. Is there no end to this boy's talents? Tell me, Tich, what are you going to do with the money?

TICH: Spend it.

SMILES: And very wise, too. Have you any idea what you'll spend it on?

TICH: First thing I'm going to do is buy my parents a nice big house and a new car.

SMILES: Now isn't that wonderful, ladies and gentlemen? His first thought is for the parents that brought him into the world, the father and mother who loved him and cared for him. Give him a big hand!

[*The audience applauds warmly*]

Will your parents be looking in, Tich? Would you like to say a few words to them?

TICH: They're here.

SMILES: They're in the audience? Well, why didn't you say so? Let's have them up, shall we? Mr and Mrs Oldfield, would you like to come onto the stage?

[FATHER *and* MOTHER *appear.* FATHER *shakes hands with the compère,* MOTHER *impulsively and tearfully embraces her son*]

SMILES: [*With a tear in his voice*] Now isn't that a moving sight, ladies and gentlemen? A mother united with her loving son.

[*He takes out a handkerchief. The audience weeps loudly*] I can understand your feelings, my dear friends. They do you credit, they really do. [*Snapping out of it*] And now, I'm sure you'd all like me to ask Mr Oldfield what he thinks of our talented victor.

FATHER: [*Puzzled*] His name's David.

SMILES: Eh? Oh, I see! The wit runs in the family. Haw! Haw! Haw! Mrs Oldfield, let's ask you, then. Are you proud of your son?

MOTHER: I am that. He's one in a million.

SMILES: In more senses than one, if you'll allow me to say so.

FATHER: He's always been a credit to us.

MOTHER: Never a bit of trouble. He's been a pleasure to bring up.

SMILES: Now isn't that nice to hear? Model parents of a model son. The prize couldn't have gone to a more deserving family. Mr and Mrs Oldfield and Tich, it's been wonderful to make your acquaintance. Take your money and good luck to you.

[*The* OLDFIELDS *leave the stage. Applause.* TICH *returns to bed and to sleep. The clapometer is removed*]

Well, it's time to bring our show to a close, ladies and gentlemen. We hope you've enjoyed it, and this is your host, Gooey Smiles, saying goodnight and sweet dreams!

[*He departs to appropriate music.* FATHER *and* MOTHER *bring on the breakfast table and two chairs for the next scene*]

[FATHER *sits at the table.* MOTHER *goes to the foot of the 'stairs'. She squawks like an angry duck*]

MOTHER: David! You David! Da-vid!

[TICH *stirs and answers sleepily*]

TICH: I'm coming.

MOTHER: Shift yourself, will you? You'll be late for school again.

[TICH *gets out of bed and starts to dress*]

MOTHER: [*To* DAD] God help him when he starts work. They'll be sacking him before he clocks on.
FATHER: Quite right, love. It's the likes of him we're fighting for, an' all.
MOTHER: Fighting! Is that what you call it? Sitting round on your backside all day?
FATHER: But I'm on strike, Elsie.
MOTHER: I shall go on strike one of these days. Then you'd look sick, the lot of you.

[*Enter* TICH]

MOTHER: Why don't you come when you're called?
TICH: I was dreaming.
MOTHER: Dreaming? You do nothing else. I wonder you bother to get up at all.
TICH: I got woken up by a terry-dactyl.
MOTHER: Don't be so damned cheeky.
TICH: [*Spotting his boiled egg*] It *was* a terry-dactyl. Look, it's left me a present.

[*He clouts it with his spoon*]

It's prehistoric, alright. I've bent me spoon.
MOTHER: That egg was fresh yesterday. Get it down you.
TICH: Bird must have been constipated, then.
MOTHER: It's all you'll get with your dad on strike.
TICH: When are you going back, dad?
FATHER: [*As though quoting*] When the employers are prepared to meet our demands.
TICH: Why don't you just go and bash 'em up? There's a picture in our history books at school of a load of mill workers

marching up to t'boss's house with clubs and the boss looking dead scared.

FATHER: We don't do that anymore. Be in trouble wi' police. I like to keep my nose clean.

TICH: Why don't you picket?

FATHER: What, me nose?

TICH: No, I mean why don't you be a picket? Stand at the gate and frighten scabs away.

FATHER: That don't do any good. Best wait for t'representatives to negotiate a settlement.

TICH: What does that mean?

FATHER: Well . . . they talk.

TICH: [*Scornfully*] Oh, talking.

MOTHER: I'll give you talking. Haven't you started that egg, yet?

TICH: I don't fancy it, mum.

MOTHER: Well, you'll have to go without, then. I don't wonder they call you 'Tich'. You won't even be as big as your dad, and *he* daren't walk over a drain for fear of disappearing down it. Get off with you, or you'll miss that bus again.

TICH: [*Standing*] Can I have twenty-five pence, dad?

MOTHER: Twenty-five blasted pence? What for?

TICH: It's school trip this afternoon. We're going to the zoo.

MOTHER: Well you'll have to miss it, then, won't you? Do you think we've come into a fortune or something?

TICH: I'll have to get it from the Poor Box, in that case.

MOTHER: Get it from what?

TICH: Poor Box. It's what they call the school fund. If your parents are too poor to pay for you, they pay for you out of the school fund.

MOTHER: You're not getting no money from no Poor Box. We'd never live it down. You're not taking no charity.

FATHER: Go and get your school bag, lad. Things'll be better, soon.

[TICH *shrugs and goes upstairs.* MOTHER *brings a tray. She addresses* FATHER]

MOTHER: Help me side this lot. Do something for a living.
FATHER: [*Complying*] Seems a pity about the zoo.
MOTHER: He's better off away from it. They'd only keep him there if he went. Pulling his blasted faces. [*They leave*]

[TICH *sits on his bed, hastily scribbling his homework*]

[*On comes* 'THORNY' BRIAR, *brisk and breezy head of Middle School. He stands behind the table as though it were a lectern*]

BRIAR: And in conclusion, boys and girls, I'd like you to know that the Headmaster is very pleased with the way the three schools are coalescing. [*He tries again*] Are amalgamating. Becoming united. [*With vibrant drama*] Through our ancient corridors has blown a Wind of Change . . .

[*From offstage comes the sound of a rushing, mighty flatulence*]

BRIAR: Who did that? WHO DID THAT? Oldfield! Where's Oldfield? [*Pause*] Not here, did you say? Not here? That's no excuse. Send him to me when he comes!

[*He stamps off, furiously*]

[*The scene becomes a classroom, seen from the class's angle. Boys and girls stroll in chattering and laughing. Enter* BARREL, PAM *and* ALLMAN. BARREL *sits on the table, which is now the teacher's table:* PAM *stands beside him. The bed is removed*]

ALLMAN: Hey, was it you, Barrel?
BARREL: [*With mock innocence*] Now would I do a thing like that?
OTHERS: Yes, you would.

BARREL: Pam, I appeal to *you.*

PAM: I wouldn't put it past you.

GIRL: Does he appeal to you, Pam?

PAM: [*Embarrassed*] Mind your own business.

GIRL: Look at her blushing.

PAM: I'm not.

ALLMAN: You could've dropped us all in it, Barrel. Thorny might've cancelled the outing.

BARREL: Not him. If he'd cancelled the outing he'd have had to do some teaching. Pity Oldfield wasn't there, though.

[*Enter* TICH]

ALLMAN: Talk o' the devil.

BARREL: Well, look what's crawled in. The only man as can walk under a dash-hound without knocking his hat off.

TICH: Shut your face, Barrel!

BARREL: Mr Snide to you, midget. Barrel to my friends. Where've you been anyway? We thought you were on strike, like your dad.

TICH: I missed the bus.

ALLMAN: Briar missed you, too – in assembly. He wants to see you.

TICH: I don't care.

BARREL: [*With a sneer*] Mighty Mouse rides again.

ALLMAN: Wheeeeeeeee! Kerpow!

[*He dive-bombs* TICH *and thumps him*]

TICH: Gerroff!

BARREL: You going to the zoo, Oldfield?

TICH: What of it?

BARREL: Should've stayed at home and saved yourself the bus fare. [*Laughter*]

BARREL: Are you getting it from school fund again?

TICH: No, I'm not.

ALLMAN: Chivers calls it [*He does a bad imitation of* CHIVERS*'s voice*] 'living orff the parish'.

BOY: That don't sound like Jammy. Tich is best at imitating.

BARREL: So are monkeys. Come on, then, Oldfield. Let's see you do Chivers.

TICH: I don't feel like it.

PAM: Go on, Tich. It'll be a giggle.

BARREL: Tell you what. You all sit in your desks and Oldfield can sit in Chivers's seat. Just to set the scene, like.

[*Encouragement from all round. After a moment's hesitation* TICH *takes the teacher's chair. Someone lends him a pair of spectacles and then the rest take their seats*]

I'll go and make sure he's not coming.

[*He goes to the door, looks out, gives a momentary start then calls blandly*]

BARREL: There's nobody in sight. Get on with it.

[BARREL *moves hurriedly to his seat.* TICH *launches into a life-like imitation of* CHIVERS]

TICH: [*As* CHIVERS] Today, I want to talk to you about the causes of the disturbances in the early nineteenth century. For about six hours.

[CHIVERS *himself enters. He stops and watches with mounting annoyance, but* TICH *fails to notice*]

Get out your pens and write down every word I say. I don't want anybody asking any questions and if anybody interrupts me he can get out and stay in. I don't want to see a single stupid face. All I'm interested in is the top of your heads.

[*On cue,* CHIVERS *clouts* TICH *on the top of his head with a book*]

TICH: Give over! [*Sees* CHIVERS] Oh, blimey!

CHIVERS: Get out of my chair, you cheeky little oaf. I suppose you think that's clever, making fun of a member of the staff.

TICH: No, sir.

CHIVERS: You're not fit to be in a decent school. We had civilized traditions before people like you came and brought us all down to your level. You can write me a hundred lines: 'I must not behave like an ill-bred guttersnipe.' Go and sit down and get out your book.

[TICH *scuttles to his seat*]

Sit up straight, the lot of you. Snide, what were we talking about last time?

BARREL: Sir, about how the workmen used to break up machines, sir.

CHIVERS: Correct. At least somebody's awake. The machines could do the work of several men so the workmen broke them up. Typical, of course, of the attitudes of the working class towards progress. Take your pens and write as I dictate. And I don't want anybody falling asleep. Do you hear that, Oldfield?

TICH: Yes, Sir.

CHIVERS: Get ready, then. 'The introduction of new machinery and the consequent increase in unemployment gave rise to widespread unrest. Unlawful gatherings took place at which the workmen aired their grievances and formulated plans of action . . .'

[*Everybody 'freezes' for a moment. This is the signal that* TICH *has gone into a daze. Like a zombie,* CHIVERS *moves away to be joined by a number of the class.* TICH *rises and stands on the table*]

TICH: [*Addressing the remainder*] Brothers, we've got to do something about it. [*Murmurs of agreement from the audience*] Our wives and kids are starving, while the bosses are stuffing themselves with chicken and chips. My dad says we should talk to them, but they just don't want to listen. I'm sick of being pushed around and clouted. It's time we taught 'em a lesson. Are you with me?

[*A roar of support*]

Let's go, then, and smash up all the machinery in the factory.

ALLMAN: But Davey, Mr Chivers has got the soldiers in. Look!

[*He points and they all look*]

TICH: Do you see that, men? It's war!

[*An anxious murmur passes through the crowd*]

BARREL: Davey, hadn't we better try talking, like your dad says?

TICH: What's the matter, Tub Guts? Are you scared?

BARREL: I've got a wife and family to think of, like you said.

TICH: And so have I, if it comes to that. [*Calls*] Pam!

PAM: [*In the crowd*] Yes, love?

TICH: What do you think I should do?

PAM: I'm right behind you, David, whatever you decide.

TICH: That's my Pam! You're a better man than any of them, even if you are a woman. Are any of you heroes coming with me, then?

[*Silence from the crowd*]

Right, I'll go by myself. [*Calling*] Chivers! Oy, Chivers! Show thy face.

[CHIVERS *appears at the door of his mill, with a line of soldiers in front of him*]

CHIVERS: Who's making all this noise? Oldfield? Is it you again? You always were a troublemaker.
TICH: I'm coming to smash those machines up, Chivers.
CHIVERS: You take one step in this direction, you ill-bred guttersnipe, and I'll order the soldiers to fire.

[*The soldiers bring their muskets to their shoulders*]

BARREL: He means what he says, Davey. Let's get out of here.
TICH: Shut your trap, Mighty Mouse. A man's got to do what a man's got to do.

[*He jumps off the table, seizes an axe from a member of the crowd*]

Right, Chivers, let's see what you're made of.

[*He starts to walk towards the soldiers*]

CHIVERS: You've asked for it, Oldfield. Fire!

[*Nothing happens*]

CHIVERS: [*Panic-stricken*] I said fire, didn't you hear me? Fire, damn you!

[TICH *halts with muskets against his chest*]

TICH: [*Calmly*] Well, comrades, are you going to fire?

[*Pause. Then the soldiers lower their muskets. The crowd cheer as the soldiers mingle with them, shaking their hands*]

TICH: [*Shouting above the noise*] Get Chivers!

[*Some of the crowd grab* CHIVERS *and bring him to* TICH]

TICH: Well, Mr Jammy Chivers. The boot's on the other foot, now, isn't it? What shall we do with him, mates?
CROWD: Hang him! Hang him!

TICH: Did you hear that, Chivers? The workers have decided to hang you from this here tree. [*He indicates the imaginary tree under which they are standing*] For crimes against our class. Have you anything to say?

[CHIVERS *drops on his knees*]

CHIVERS: Have mercy on me, for God's sake. I'm too old to die.

TICH: Get to your feet, you silly twit.

CHIVERS: [*Rising*] I'll cancel that imposition!

TICH: You should have thought about that before. It's too late now. Right, lads, let's proceed with the execution.

[*He mimes slipping a noose round* CHIVERS'*s neck and throwing the rope over a tree-branch above. All the children return to their seats and start to drum on their desk lids. The drumming gets louder and faster, reaches a climax and ceases abruptly. There is silence and stillness for a moment. Then* CHIVERS *returns to 'life' and turns on* TICH]

CHIVERS: Oldfield, how much longer are you going to keep me hanging around? I'm waiting for an answer.

TICH: What did you say?

CHIVERS: Get to your feet, you insolent lout. Bring me your notebook. [*He scans it briefly*] Two sentences. Two miserable sentences. [*He beats time to this on* TICH'*s head*] You've been dreaming again, all the time I've been talking. Well, you can just borrow somebody else's book and copy out the notes from that. And you can bring them to me in the morning, along with that imposition. Is that clear?

TICH: Yes, sir.

CHIVERS: Go back to your place; you make me sick. The rest of you, put your books away. There'll be no homework tonight because of this ridiculous outing. It's not my idea, I assure you! I don't know what the school is coming to.

[*He sweeps out. The class give a muffled cheer*]

[*Enter* MISS FECKLESS, *youngish, overdressed and anxious. Her authority is negligible. She carries a list of names and when she appears the children rise, carrying their chairs, and file past her as though getting onto a bus. They place their chairs in twos so that the final effect is of a cross section through it. There also enters the* DRIVER, *who picks up the table and places it at the front of the vehicle as the engine, taking one of the chairs there for himself. At the end of the queue are* BARREL, PAM *and* TICH.]

MISS F.: Darrel Snide, Pamela Russell and David Oldfield.

[BARREL *sits by the window,* PAM *next to him*]

MISS F.: What's that book you've got, David?
TICH: James Bond, Miss.
MISS F.: Oh, dear. I don't think you should be reading that. The Headmaster wouldn't approve. Keep it in your pocket, there's a good boy.

[TICH *shrugs and takes a solitary seat behind* BARREL *and* PAM]

MISS F.: Are we all here, then?
CLASS: [*In a rude sing-song*] Yes, Miss Feckless.
MISS F.: We're all here, driver. Hadn't we better get started?
DRIVER: [*With a leer*] Whenever you're ready, darling.
CLASS: Ooooooooh! [*Kissing noises*]

[*The engine starts and the children cheer. By their movements they show that the vehicle is gathering speed.* TICH *takes out his book and starts to read*]

BARREL: Can we sing, Miss?
MISS F.: [*Half rising*] Oh, if you must. But please keep it quiet. And please keep it respectable. [*Sits again*]

BARREL: [*Loudly*]
Oh, dear, what can the matter be,
Fanny Feckless locked in a lavatory,

[*The rest join in*]

She was there from Monday to Saturday,
Nobody knew she was there.

[MISS FECKLESS *rises with a fierce look on her face and an air of uncharacteristic authority. In her hand is a pistol*]

MISS F.: Silence!

[*Silence falls*]

Now listen to me for a change. Sit still and shut up. Allman, I'm talking to you.

ALLMAN: [*In meek amazement*] Yes, Miss.

MISS F.: The Captain and I have something to say to you.

[*The* DRIVER *comes out of the 'cockpit'*]

MISS F.: We have taken the places of the real pilot and the air hostess. Our mission is to kidnap one of the passengers. She thinks we don't know who she is, but we have seen through her disguise. Captain.

[*The* DRIVER *seizes* PAM *and drags her to the front of the bus. Expressions of surprise from the rest*]

Quiet! [*To* PAM] You are coming with us, my dear.

[*The* DRIVER *mimes putting a parachute onto her*]

This is the Princess Pamelana. Her father is the King of Cleethorpes and will pay a handsome ransom. I'm afraid we'll have to leave you now. We're flying over our secret hideout.

Goodbye, you little horrors. Enjoy your trip to the next world. Open the door, Captain.

[*The* DRIVER *does this. He and* MISS FECKLESS *grab* PAM *by the wrists*]

PAM: [*Screaming*] Help me, Darrel! Help!
BARREL: I can't do nothing, Pam.
TICH: But I can, Olga, can't I?
MISS F.: Great heavens, it's Tich Bond!
TICH: Let them go, you rotten twits. The game's up.
MISS F.: Jump, Captain, quickly!
MISS F. and DRIVER: One, two, three . . .

[TICH *races forward and grabs* PAM *as the villains jump and float away shaking their fists. Someone closes the door*]

PAM: You saved me, Tich. You're wonderful.
BARREL: What about this plane, then, Mr Wonderful? We ain't got a pilot.
TICH: You'll have to make do with me, then, won't you?
BOY: But you've never flown a plane, Tich, have you?
TICH: I've ridden a trolley. It can't be much different. Go back to your seats, the lot of you, and fasten yourselves in. You can look after Pam for me, Snide.

[*The rest take their seats as* TICH *takes the controls*]

TICH: Going down – now!

[*All lean forward as the plane descends. Suddenly, they lurch to the right*]

BOY: Wing's fallen off!

[*They lurch the other way*]

GIRL: Now the other one's gone.

TICH: Th'undercarriage's jammed as well. Stand by for a belly flop.

[*As the plane hits the ground, the passengers bounce up and down in their seats, and finally come to rest*]

PAM: He's done it! I knew he would.

[*All babble excitedly.* TICH *emerges from the cockpit and holds up his hands for attention*]

TICH: I know how you feel, but it's all part of the day's work. Get outside right away before the thing blows up.

[*The passengers file out past him. As they do so,* MISS FECKLESS *and the* DRIVER *reappear and stand outside the door*]

MISS F.: Come on, David. You're always the last, aren't you? You are a dream. Now don't forget, boys and girls, I want you back by half-past five and please don't be late, and please be careful with the animals. Have you all got your lunch packs?

CLASS: Yes, Miss Feckless.

MISS F.: Good. We'll see you later, then, driver.

DRIVER: Right you are, darling.

[*He removes the table. The children dismantle the bus, placing three or four of the chairs down front to represent a bench seat.* MISS FECKLESS *wanders off and the party disperses*]

[*The stage remains empty for a few seconds and the air is filled with jungle noises. Then on comes* TICH, *hacking his way through undergrowth and creepers. He stops and wipes his brow. Then he throws back his head, beats his chest and gives a Tarzan call. An imaginary* APE *lands at his feet. In the background the* KEEPER *enters and watches, seeing only* TICH]

TICH: Me – Tarzan; you – brother.

[*He hugs the* APE *and they do a dance together. Suddenly* TICH *spots the* KEEPER *and he stops in embarrassment*]

KEEPER: They'll be putting you away, Shorthouse.
TICH: I didn't know you were there.
KEEPER: I could see that. Who d'you think you are, then? Tarzan? More like Shaun the Leprechaun.
TICH: I was only pretending.
KEEPER: You want some horse muck in your shoes, make you grow a bit. Are you with this school party?
TICH: Yeh.
KEEPER: I hate kids. Feeding crocodiles wi' bubbly gum and drawing pictures on the rhino's It's not funny, I tell you. Don't know how to treat animals, kids don't.
TICH: No use looking at me. I never touched 'em.
KEEPER: You're all as bad. What have you come for, anyway?
TICH: We've got to write about 'em. Poems and that.
KEEPER: Poems? What a waste of time. You want to do a day's work for a change. I was earning me living at your age.
TICH: It's not my fault.
KEEPER: You get things too easy these days. I deserve my money, every miserable penny of it. I've got to clean monkeys out now. Like a job, would you?
TICH: I wouldn't mind.
KEEPER: Get on with your poetry, Shakespeare. And make sure it's paper you write it on.

[*He exits.* TICH *takes out a notebook and pencil and sits on the bench*]

TICH: [*To himself*]
A monkey is an animal
That swings from bough to bough . . .

[*His mouth silently runs through the alphabet to find a rhyme, cow, dow, fow, gow etc. Enter* BARREL *and* PAM *carrying packed lunches*]

BARREL: Now here's an interesting specimen, Pamela. If it had a brain it'd be almost human. [*He holds out his hand to* TICH] Puss, puss, puss!

TICH: Get lost, Barrel.

BARREL: Did you hear that, Pamela? Obviously dangerous. You sit here and I'll protect you.

[*They sit on the seat,* BARREL *next to* TICH. *Barrel puts his packed lunch on the seat next to* TICH *and opens it.* PAM *opens hers on her lap.* TICH *tries not to look.* BARREL *takes out a sandwich*]

BARREL: What's first on the menu, then? Cheese butties. What have you got, Pam?

PAM: Pork.

BARREL: Hear that, Oldfield? She's eating one of your relatives.

PAM: Haven't you got any sandwiches, Tich?

TICH: Didn't bring any.

PAM: Would you like one of mine?

BARREL: You mustn't feed the animals. It's against the regulations.

TICH: I'm not bothered.

BARREL: There you are, you see. Oldfield's not bothered. He doesn't want a delicious cheese sandwich, flavoured with pickles, do you, Oldfield?

[*He takes a huge bite*]

Mmmmmmmmm! Smashing! Bit of tomato to go with it.

[*He eats a tomato.* TICH *is suffering intensely. Unnoticed, an* APE *appears in the background.* BARREL *finishes his sandwich. He turns to* PAM]

BARREL: Like a drop of fizz, Pam?
PAM: Oh, yes, please.
BARREL: Hold your cup out, then.

[*While he pours the lemonade, the* APE *steals a banana from his lunch pack and starts to eat it.* BARREL *takes a swig from his bottle and turns again to his lunch pack*]

BARREL: Hey! Have you been at my picnic?
TICH: What do you mean?
BARREL: There was a banana there a minute ago.
TICH: I haven't had it.

[BARREL *seizes him by the shirt front*]

I want that banana back, Oldfield.

[TICH *struggles to his feet and tries to pull away.* BARREL *also rises*]

TICH: I haven't got your rotten banana.
BARREL: If you've eaten it, you thieving little swine . . .

[*The* APE *grabs* PAM *by the shoulders. She screams.* BARREL *turns, jumps and lets go of* TICH]

PAM: Get it off! Get it off!

[*The* APE *pulls* PAM *off the seat and embraces her. The sandwiches slip to the ground.* PAM *squeals, hysterically*]

BARREL: Let go! Good dog! Let go – please.

[*The* APE *growls at him*]

BARREL: I'm off. [*He flees*]

[TICH *watches with a dazed look as though he is not sure whether he is dreaming or not. Then suddenly he starts to beat his chest like Tarzan. The* APE *turns and looks at him quizzically*]

TICH: Me – Tarzan! You – brother!

[*The* APE *bares his teeth.* TICH *stiffens with fright*]

TICH: Fizzin' 'ell! It doesn't work!

[*He turns and runs. The* APE *pursues him round the stage. Finally* TICH *falls over and the* APE *places a foot on him and starts to beat his chest.* PAM *hops about the while shouting for help. On comes the* KEEPER. *He crosses to the* APE, *takes him by the hand and pulls him away*]

KEEPER: Come on, Bimbo, come with Uncle Philip. There's a good boy. He's quite harmless when he knows you. He likes a bit of fun, that's all. Are you all right, Shorthouse?

TICH: He's torn me shirt.

KEEPER: That's nothing.

TICH: Nothing? My mum'll kill me. Then she'll come here and play hell.

KEEPER: Look, Shorthouse, couldn't you tell her you tore it on a fence or something? I mean, she doesn't have to know it was an ape, does she? Cause a lot of trouble if anybody found out he escaped. I could swear blind I locked that cage, I really could. Not like me at all. Here, take this lot and keep your mouth shut, O.K.?

[*He gives* TICH *a handful of loose change*]

TICH: Gosh, thanks.

KEEPER: Think on, Shorthouse. Let's go home, Bimbo. Uncle Philip take him home? Come on, lovie.

[*He leads the* APE *away*]

TICH: [*To* PAM] One pound and forty-five pence.

PAM: Serves him right. Shove it in your pocket before he changes his mind.

TICH: Are you all right?
PAM: I can't stop shivering.
TICH: Better sit down a minute.

[*They sit on the seat*]

Your sandwiches are all mucky.
PAM: I don't want 'em anyway.

[*Pause*]

TICH: I could afford a proper meal. Two meals. In t'café.
PAM: I couldn't eat a thing, honest.

[*Enter* BARREL]

BARREL: I went to get help. Somebody had to do something, didn't they? You O.K. Pam?
PAM: Bit shook up, but I'm not hurt.
BARREL: Like a coffee? Best thing for nerves.
PAM: Wouldn't mind.
BARREL: Come on, then. There's a machine over there.
PAM: What about Tich?
BARREL: Oldfield can look after the stuff for us. Tell you what, Oldfield, you can have all the sandwiches that fell on the ground.

[*He puts his arm suavely and protectively round* PAM *and leads her away.* TICH *watches them go. Then he takes the money out of his pocket, looks at it, clenches it furiously in his fist and rams it decisively back into his pocket. Then he shouts*]

You stinking, fat, big-headed Sex Maniac!

[*He picks up* BARREL's *sandwiches, grins fiendishly and shakes them out all over the ground. Then he exits jauntily*]

[*Enter* TICH's MOTHER *with a dustpan and brush. She hums*

happily to herself, even, amazingly, when she cleans up the sandwiches. DAD *brings on the table, dismantles the 'bench' and goes upstairs. When she has finished,* MOTHER *sits on a chair, and looks at a woman's magazine.* TICH *enters fearfully and stands by the door.*]

MOTHER: [*Purely for information*] Where've you been?
TICH: I had to stay in, and then I missed the bus.
MOTHER: [*With mock severity*] Eeh, you naughty lad. What are we going to do with you? Have you had any tea?
TICH: No, mum.
MOTHER: [*Bounding up*] Well what would you like, then? We've not much in, but you're welcome to what there is. Like a nice boiled egg?
TICH: [*Shrinking away*] You feeling all right, mum?
MOTHER: Right as rain. Why shouldn't I be?
TICH: Where's dad?
MOTHER: He's upstairs.
TICH: Is *he* all right?
MOTHER: Course he's all right. What's the matter with you?

[*Enter* FATHER]

FATHER: Hello, Davey, lad. You all right, then?
MOTHER: Don't you start.
TICH: I'm all right, dad. It's mum. She's all different.
FATHER: That's not surprising, is it, lad?
TICH: What do you mean?
FATHER: Didn't you tell him, Elsie?
MOTHER: I haven't had a chance.
FATHER: Strike's over, Davey. We've got a rise, a big 'un, too.
TICH: A rise? That's great! Did you hang the boss?
FATHER: [*Laughing*] We negotiated a settlement. If I had any ready money, we'd celebrate.

TICH: I've got some money, dad. A quid.

MOTHER: A quid? Where did you get that from?

TICH: Found it.

FATHER: Been a good day all round, hasn't it? What shall we spend it on, then, Davey?

TICH: Let's get some chicken and chips.

FATHER: Chicken and chips! I could just go a dollop of that. Nip out and get it, Davey.

TICH: I got a better idea. Let's go and have it in the café. I've always wanted to eat in there. Save mum washing up.

MOTHER: [*To* FATHER] Pity *you* didn't think of that. I'll go and get my coat. David's right, we'll eat in style for once.

[*She exits*]

TICH: Wish I could find a quid every day.

FATHER: That only happens in dreams, lad. Best to settle for what you've got. Be back to normal tomorrow.

MOTHER: [*Calling from offstage, with a hint of impatience*] Are you coming, then?

FATHER: Before tomorrow if we don't look sharp. Lead the way, Rockefeller. Mustn't keep her waiting.

[*They go out*]

Apples

Cecil P. Taylor

Cast

KIDS 1–18

Dedicated to Jim, with love . . .

Apples

SCENE: On the back of the stage an idyllic sunrise scene is projected. Some uplifting theme music is playing, romantically and swelling up. The KIDS *walk on to the stage, moving towards the rising sun.*

[*To the audience*]

KID 1: [*Indicating his mates*] Kids.
KID 2: [*Indicating rising sun*] Sun rising.
KID 4: We are on the point of leaving school.
KID 5: The sun is rising for us.
KID 6: Our whole future's in front of us.
KID 1: *Practically* our whole future.
KID 6: We are walking towards the sun.
KIDS ALL: [*Singing*]
There is a happy land,
Far, far away.
KID 7: You know the kind of thing . . .
KID 1: Got to start somewhere, haven't you?

[*To each other*]

KID 2: The sun thing's all right.
KID 3: Nice . . .

KID 4: Music's nice.
. . . So

[*To audience*]

KID 9: So the teacher . . .
KID 10: I am the teacher.
How do you do, everybody.
I am about to shake hands with my pupils,
Who are on the point of leaving the warm, kind shelter of the school.

[*Turning to pupils*]

Cheers, please . . .
KIDS: Hurray . . .
KID 10: And seek their fortunes
In the world that lies
Before them.
KIDS: Cheers . . .
KID 10: Wait a minute!

[*Slide of school hall. Assembly*]

KID 10: Children,
My dear pupils,
Good luck.
The world is yours,
A tree heavy with berries
To pluck as you will.
KIDS: Goodbye dear teacher . . .
KID 10: Goodbye . . . Goodbye . . . Goodbye . . .
KIDS: [*To each other*] Well that's done, anyway . . .
KID 11: So we went east,
Towards the beckoning sun . . .

KID 12: Our old teacher
Framed in the doorway of the school,
Still waving to us . . .
Till we had passed out of sight . . .
KID 12: Nice man.
KID 13: Canny.
KID 14: Not really a stupid old bastard.
KID 15: Not that you'd notice.
KID 1: As you heard from our old teacher,
There's a tree hanging around somewhere,
Waiting for us,
Heavy with apples . . .
KID 3: If he said so it must be there.
But nobody could see it . . .
KID 4: [*To others*]
Must be somewhere
He knows what he's on about . . .
What you call him again?
KID 5: [*To others*]
Our old teacher . . .
KID 6: If we all got on each other's shoulders,
Made a pyramid,
And the lightest got on top . . .
KID 7: And we had a look through a telescope . . .
KID 9: Might be able to see it.

[*They make a pyramid. Try a telescope*]

KID 10: I see it . . . I see it . . . I see it . . .
KID 11: He got a bit excited you see . . . Jumping up and down . . .

[*The pyramid collapses in chaos*]

KID 10: Great, big fantastic, fabulous apple tree . . .

KID 12: So you said . . .
KID 10: Should see the apples . . .
KID 13: Big as a football . . .?
KID 10: Bigger . . . Big as your whole life . . .
. . . That way . . .
KID 14: That's the way we're going,
Towards the sun.
KID 15: Yeah. But we know definitely, now,
Don't we?
KID 16: [*To audience*]
So it was definitely established,
Our dear teacher was right.
There was an apple tree
Heavy with apples –

[*Slide of an apple tree, heavy with fruit. Maybe a chorus from the* KIDS *of a popular song*]

KID 14: [*to audience*]
Just to give you a breather
Before the next
Incredible,
Terrifying,
Fantastic,
Fabulous scene . . .
KID 1: We hadn't got far,
After making sure
There was an apple tree.
KID 2: Everybody chuff,
There *was* one.
Stepping it out
Fast as they could
When . . .
KID 16: [*Steps out and blocks their advance*]

KID 16: [*To* KIDS]
I am a great big, thick,
Forest of giant
Thorn trees.
Every spiked branch
Woven into the next.
Impassable
By all.
KID 1: [*To audience*] Here's the big point . . .
KID 16: By all
Whose I.Q.
Is below 126.843 . . . Good afternoon.
KID 1: [*To audience*] See what I mean . . .
KID 2: [*To others*] Alas, our I.Q.'s.
Are all 126.842.
KID 3: The Forest said very nastily to us, as soon as he heard that . . .
FOREST: That's *your* hard luck, mates!
KID 4: [*To audience*]
To make sure you get the point
Of the forest
We ask him:
KID 5: Our nice old teacher,
Never told us anything
About a forest lying
Between us
And the great apple tree.
What do they call you?

[FOREST *turns his back on the* KIDS, *exhibiting placard for the audience to read:* '*OPPORTUNITY FOREST*']

KID 6: There must be *some* way
Through you!

[*The* FOREST *indicates* KID 7. KID 7 *turns round to show the audience his placard*]

'Education Commission Gate. Certificate Holders only allowed through. No Fire permitted.'

KID 6: [*To audience*]
Alas, we had
Not one certificate
Between us.
KID 9: It seemed
The apple tree
That beckoned us
To enjoy its fruit,
Would never be reached by us . . .
KID 8: [*To* FOREST]
Our kind teacher
Told us a story
About Bruce
And a spider.
KID 9: The moral was,
Try, and try again.
KID 10: Never give up.
KID 11: Where there is life there is hope.
EDUCATION GATE: I am not allowed to enter
Into any discussion,
Whatsoever,
With unsuccessful
Entrants.
KID 12: Is that the only way through you?
But . . .
CERTIFICATES GATE: No use asking me,
Is it?
I'm only a gate.

Can you not read?

[*And he points to* KID 18 *– a placard hangs from his neck: 'APPLE TREE INFORMATION CENTRE. MAPS, CHARTS, GUIDEBOOKS AND SOUVENIRS AVAILABLE INSIDE'*]

KID 18: [*To* KIDS] Haven't a Certificate between you?

[*They shake their heads*]

Thought so.
Never get through him.
KID 1: No.

[INFORMATION CENTRE: *handing out postcards*]

That's the apple tree.
Lovely spot.
KID 2: So we've heard.
INFORMATION: The apples! . . . Big as your life . . .
KID 3: Not much use to us, are they?
INFORMATION: How's that?
What did your old teacher say?
KID 4: Good luck . . .
INFORMATION: Bruce and The Spider,
I'm talking about.
KID 5: Bruce and The Spider.
INFORMATION: Use your eyes . . .
KIDS: Like how?
INFORMATION: Other paths through the forest . . .
KIDS: You reckon?
INFORMATION: I'm *telling* you. I'm the Information Centre aren't I?
KID 6: [*To audience*] He pointed all round the forest . . .

INFORMATION: Before you go,
Give us a song;
For me
And the audience . . .
KID 6: How about [*He names a popular song*]
That always goes down very well.

[*They march off singing the chorus*]

KID 7: Till we got to the first gate.

[*Slide of interior of a bank*]

KID: I am gate Number One.
Pleased to meet you.
KID 8: Just want to get through to the apple tree.
GATE: Uh, huh. Uh, huh . . . How much have your fathers in the bank?
Shares . . . Unit Trusts . . . Property owned . . . Rented . . . as well as occupied by owner . . . Add it all up.
Get it signed by your Bank Manager . . . And you're through here like a shot . . . Minimum totals for me . . . £42,000 . . . But down the road there's a gate'll let you through for £16,000 . . . And I hear, further down, there's supposed to be one opening up at £10,000 . . .
KID 9: Alas, between us and all our fathers, mothers, grandfathers and grandmothers we hadn't ten thousand new pennies.
KID 10: We skipped by the three Bank Gates . . .

[*They do this*]

KID 11: Remembering what our old teacher told us
About Bruce and The Spider . . .
KID 12: I said the sun seemed to be getting a bit duller.
KID 13: But I said
It was just her imagination.

KID 14: I am Gate Number Four.
Nice to see you.

[*Slide of market or Stock Exchange*]

To see you nice.
KID 1: Heard that before somewhere . . .
KID 14: I'm not interested in how much your father or mother or grannie has in the bank,
Or how much he earns a year.
KID 2: That's more like it.
KID 14: I'm just interested in you yourselves,
As talented kids.
KID 3: Great.
KID 14: Want to get the apple tree?
Great.
All you do is
Do a turn for me.
Make the grade,
And you're through.

[*A row of guitars . . . pianos . . . painting easels . . . drawing boards . . . etc.* GATE FOUR *passes a guitar round the* KIDS *who pass it round each other. Eventually one tries to play it . . .*]

GATE 4: [*Taking it off him*] I'll write to you.
Next . . .
KID 5: [*Scrawling a poem on the blackboard*]
If you walk up
The hill road
That leads up
Through the town –
GATE 4: [*Checking on his list*] Sorry . . . No market for poetry just now . . .
KID 6: [*Sings*]

I see Herring,
I see Herring,
Great, great shoals,
Of shining Herring.
Cast your nets,
Oh, cast them quickly!
I see Herring!
I see Herring!

GATE 4: Very nice . . . Next, please.

KID 7: [*Takes up a football . . . dribbles.* GATE 4 *takes the ball off him*]

GATE 4: Anybody else fancies a turn with the ball?

[KID 8 *tries it . . . Another tries the piano . . . Somebody tries to draw . . .*]

GATE 4: [*Dismissing them all*]
Very interesting. Yes.
Have a good journey.

KID 9: Before we go.
I can't see any other gates.
Where's the next one?

GATE 4: That's it, isn't it?
I'm the last gate.
Last
But by no means least.

KID 10: But we've got to get through to the apple tree.

[GATE 4 *turns his back and ignores them*]

KID 11: Bruce and The Spider.

KID 12: Yeah. Bruce and The Spider.

KID 11: Had a great idea . . .

KID 2: We can't be stuck here for ever. Can we?
I mean, the apple tree's there.

The teacher said
It's there.

KID 3: I saw it.

KID 4: We saw postcards of it.

KID 2: It's for everybody,
Isn't it . . . ?
It's just a case of getting to it.

KID 4: [*With great irony*] That's all!

KID 2: We'll ask God.
The teacher says:
If you're up against it,
And you don't know what to do,
There's a path that's always open
For every me and you.
God . . .

KID 3: Dad says better,
If you want anything done,
You should go right to the top.

KID 4: The Duke of Northumberland.

KID 5: He's only up the road.

KID 6: We went to Alnwick Castle.

KID 7: I am the Duke of Northumberland,
Delighted to meet you all.
But I wish you'd stop throwing
Your empty chip bags
All round my courtyard.

KID 8: This apple tree . . .

DUKE: Smashing.

KID 9: So we hear . . .

DUKE: An apple a day keeps the doctor away . . .

KID 10: We can't get to it.

DUKE: That's a shame. Isn't that a shame.
My teacher always said:

If you're up against it . . .
And you don't know what to do . . .
KIDS: Yeah . . . ours too . . .
Ta-ra . . .
DUKE: Goodbye . . . Remember what I said about these
Empty chip bags.
KID 11: So we went into the old church.
KID 12: I am God.
Good evening.
I like this old church.
A bit cold
And lonely
But still,
Beggars can't be choosers.
What can I do for you?
If it's the apple tree . . .
Do not ask me . . .
The number of people who keep
Bothering me about that apple tree!
I wish I'd never created the bloody thing.
God in heaven!
Don't ask me about
How to get to apple trees.
It's nothing to do with me
People do what they want to do.
Don't they?
That's the whole idea.
KID 13: You no ideas how to get there, then, God?
GOD: You tried the Bishop?
They seem to know a lot about these things.
Yes.
You try the Bishop.
I'm telling you.

A mine of information,
The old Bishop.

KID 14: The Bishop said:

BISHOP: [*Eating an apple*]
Don't worry about the apple tree,
My dear children.
If you are meant to eat of the fruit of
That great apple tree,
Eat of the fruit you will.
If you are not meant to . . .
Remember,
This is us just *passing through*
This world.
A preparation for the *real* world
to come . . .

KID 1: So we went on right down the road.

KID 2: The Queen said:

QUEEN: The apples are not all they're made out to be.
But see the Prime Minister.

P. MINISTER: I am the Prime Minister.
How do you do?
If you refuse to learn French,
German
And other essential foreign languages,
I can't see
What I can possibly do for you.
Have you had a word with God?

KID 4: The Mayor said:

MAYOR: It's no use asking me.
I don't know what
The bloody apple tree looks like.

KID 5: I said:
Why don't we go back to the teacher?

Maybe we've got something wrong.
KID 6: But when we got back to the teacher.
KID 7: [*To audience*]
Hullo again.
Remember me.
I'm the Teacher.
I'm very busy.
With a new lot of pupils
Teaching them about
What to do when they find the berry tree . . .

[*To the new pupil*]

When you come to the berry tree,
You'll find it heavy with fruit.
Now there are all kinds of berries on it . . .
Red . . . Pink . . . Green . . . Yellow . . .
KID 8: [*To audience*] He was too busy
To speak to us.
KID 9: So we went on.
After a bit
When we got further and further
Away
From God and the Queen . . .
When we asked people about the apple tree
They said:
KID 10: Never heard of it.
KID 11: [*To* 10] Did your teacher never tell you about
This great apple tree?
Apples as big as your life?
KID 10: Never heard of it.
If you're hungry,
There's a chippie over there.
KID 12: There was a chippie over there.

KID 13: I'm a Chippie
Good evening.
I'm frying tonight.
KID 14: Fourteen bags of chips please.
CHIPPIE: Sorry to mention this,
But in these hard times,
Chippies like everybody else
Have to be careful.
Can I see the colour of your money?
KID 1: Don't tell me
We can't even get a bag of chips!
KID 2: They haven't *another* forest,
You've got to go through
Before you get a bag of chips?
CHIPPIE: [*Pointing to advert 'Machine Turners Wanted. Good Wages. Apply Now'*]:
If you hurry up
There's still a few jobs left.
Be able to afford *three* bags of chips a day
If you're taken on there.
Cod on a Friday night.

[*Slide of a factory*]

KID 5: We raced each other.
For the jobs . . .
I was one of the first . . .
KID 6: *I* was the first.
KID 7: I was second . . .

[*The* KIDS *who get jobs take their places at the machine, turning handles*]

KID 8: [*To the* KIDS *working*]
If they can't take us all on,

Nobody should start.
They're splitting us up.
KID 9: You're just saying that
Because you were one of the last.
KID 10: [*To audience*]:
After a bit,
We forgot our old mates' faces.
The machine keeps you busy.
And the wind.
KID 11: A great wind came up . . .
Blowing you off your feet . . .
Unless you held on to somebody . . .

[*A wind blowing now. The* KIDS *grab on to a partner, mostly boy to girl, girl to boy*]

KID 12: It was all right.
Once you grabbed hold of somebody.
KID 13: The girls held on to the boys,
And the boys to the girls.
KID 14: You could stand up stronger
Against the wind,
That way.
Fitted closer
Together.
KID 1: The wind never stops now.
KID 2: But everybody in the end
Got a job
Turning the handles.
KID 3: Chips every day . . . Good laughs all the time. [*They sing a song*]
KID 4: Yesterday a bunch of kids came to us.
KID 5: Yes. That was funny.

[*The* KIDS *separate into* NEW KIDS]

KID 6: We have just left
The warm kind shelter
Of our school.
KID 7: Can you direct us, please.
To the great apple tree . . .

[*The* OLD KIDS *look at them, puzzled*]

KID 8: [*To audience*]
Didn't know what
They were talking about.
KID 9: I said to them:
WHAT apple tree . . .?

[*The* KIDS *walk out, through the audience, singing*]

Voyage of a Lifetime

Trevor Harvey

Cast

BENJAMIN KNOWER
MARTHA, his wife
His sons: SIMON, PETER, JOHN

RUTH, Peter's wife
MARY, John's fiancée
PHILLIP, a family friend
THE BUSINESSMAN
THREE FEMALE NEIGHBOURS
Three male neighbours: SID, GEORGE, BERT

R.S.P.C.A. OFFICIAL
MINISTRY OF WORKS OFFICIAL
MINISTRY OF AVIATION OFFICIAL
CUSTOMS AND EXCISE OFFICIAL

TWO MONKEYS
TWO ELEPHANTS
TWO SHEEP
TWO PENGUINS
SNAKE
FOX
BEAR
LION
DOG
COW

VARIOUS OTHER ANIMALS

A musical score, specially written for the play by Anthony Foster, is available on hire

Voyage of a Lifetime

SCENE: Knower's back garden. A rocket is being built and is visible backstage, centre. There are several packing cases and boxes scattered about the stage. On one of these sits the BUSINESSMAN *watching* KNOWER *who is busy at work – hammering, tightening screws, examining his plans and measuring.* THREE FEMALE NEIGHBOURS *are standing behind a piece of moveable fencing, stage left. They seem very angry, but* KNOWER *does not notice them.*

FIRST NEIGHBOUR: Bang! Bang! Bang! He's been working all night! I've hardly been to sleep for the noise.

SECOND NEIGHBOUR: It's not good enough – you should start a petition.

THIRD NEIGHBOUR: Well, I've complained to the council, but what can they do? He takes no notice whatever. No consideration for his neighbours, that's his trouble.

SECOND NEIGHBOUR: Has he always been like that?

FIRST NEIGHBOUR: No – it's only since he had this dream. It's changed him completely.

THIRD NEIGHBOUR: Sounds as if he ought to have psychiatric help, if you ask me. Going off his rocker!

FIRST NEIGHBOUR: You see, he says it's the will of Alpha the Almighty. There's going to be a flood or something, and we've all to give up our bingo and football pools and ask Alpha to forgive us!

SECOND NEIGHBOUR: Ooh-er!

FIRST NEIGHBOUR: He says the rocket will take a few of us to another planet, to start all over again!

THIRD NEIGHBOUR: He'll be lucky if it manages to get as far as the rooftops. He's completely round the bend.

SECOND NEIGHBOUR: Not a very good example to his children.

FIRST NEIGHBOUR: Well, as far as I can tell, they seem to be humouring him and lending him a hand.

SECOND NEIGHBOUR: Really! Then his wife should put a stop to it, if she's any kind of a mother to her children. Wouldn't catch me playing up to my Joe like that. On the other hand, you wouldn't catch my Joe making anything in his back garden, either. He knows his place – down at the pub each evening!

THIRD NEIGHBOUR: Well, that's the proper place for a man. I mean, it's natural, isn't it? Better than making a racket like he does for twenty-four hours a day . . .!

[*Song* – All Day Long – *sung by the* THREE NEIGHBOURS]

1. All day long
It's bang, bang, bang!
At night he makes
A dreadful clang!
He never seems to take a break!
He keeps our neighbourhood awake!

2. We complain
About the noise,
And rude remarks
By little boys
Are crayon'd on his outside wall,
But it has no effect at all!

3. Day by day
   It's cling, clang, clung!
   We shall be glad
   When he is done!
   The noise will drive us all to drink!
   We've hardly time to hear us think!

4. All day long
   It's bang, bang, bang!
   At night he makes
   A dreadful clang!
   He never seems to take a break!
   He keeps our neighbourhood awake!

[*They exit left, taking fence.* THREE MEN *enter, right, with beer mugs and a portable bar*]

GEORGE: Evening, Sid.
SID: Hello, George. Escaped from the missus again?
GEORGE: Escaped from that infernal row, you mean.
BERT: Yes, it's getting a bit much, isn't it?
GEORGE: A bit much! I should say so! Well past one o'clock before I managed to get to sleep again.
BERT: All right for him, but not all right for your ordinary man.
GEORGE: No, he can sleep whenever he wants. He's not ruled by the clock, like us.
SID: Right. I mean, if you're not down to the Social Security by ten-fifteen, you have to wait all flipping day.
GEORGE: Doesn't give you a chance to snatch a quick half at lunchtime.
BERT: Or the money to pay for it.
SID: No – and I missed the first two races yesterday through him. Overslept I did, and by the time I got down to Social Security, collected my money and stuck my nose in at the bookmaker's,

it was two-fifteen. Missed a couple of sure winners there. He's costing me money, that's what he's doing.

GEORGE: He's breaking up my home. Doris hasn't stopped nagging ever since he's started his hammering. It's like having a wife and a mother-in-law rolled into one.

SID: Oh, I pity you, mate.

BERT: And what about me? My missus has been on to me about making things.

GEORGE: Making things?

BERT: Yes, a right little handyman this Knower bloke has turned out to be. 'You never make anything for me,' she says.

SID: What would she want with a flipping rocket?

BERT: I don't know, but you know my Edna. Never satisfied. Anything anyone else has got, she wants it too.

SID: I don't know why he doesn't pack it in. Why can't he stick to football pools or gardening, instead of messing about with rockets?

GEORGE: Quite right, Sid. You never said a truer word . . .

[*Song* – All Day Long – *sung by the* THREE MEN]

1. All the men
Want here is peace;
We want that row
At last to cease!
But will he stop? Oh no, not he!
He spoils our football on T.V.

2. We come down
Here to the pub,
To have a drink
And pay our sub;
Then off we roll back home again,
And listen to our wives complain!

[*The* THREE MEN *exit right with bar. The* BUSINESSMAN *rises, makes notes and looks more closely at the rocket*]

BUSINESSMAN: And it's coming along nicely, Mr Knower?

KNOWER: Well – I'm quite satisfied.

BUSINESSMAN: So you should be – it's very well designed.

KNOWER: I can't take the credit for that. It was Alpha the Almighty who showed me the blueprint in a dream.

BUSINESSMAN: But He couldn't have managed all this without you. You must be proud of yourself.

KNOWER: Yes – I suppose I am, in a way. It's an honour to be chosen by Alpha to help save the human race. The only trouble is – they don't want to be saved. Everybody laughs at me – or moans about the noise. It's a wonder they can hear it above their parties and televisions and record players. But my wife and family support me – and you don't know what a comfort it has been to have you coming round here each day and showing such an interest in my work.

BUSINESSMAN: The pleasure has been all mine, I assure you.

KNOWER: Nonsense! You've made me realize I'm not what the neighbours think I am – a silly old man, playing a game. The questions you've asked about the working of this ship have been very helpful to me.

BUSINESSMAN: And to me, dear Mr Knower. If only you knew *how* helpful!

KNOWER: [*Pause*] You'll be joining us for the journey?

BUSINESSMAN: No – I'm afraid not. I'm just a poor sinner and it's too late for me to change my ways now. Besides, I don't think I could stand the pace of rushing around up there. I'll be back to see you before you leave.

[*Enter* MRS KNOWER, *carrying a bale of hay*]

MRS KNOWER: Benjamin – [*She sees the* BUSINESSMAN] oh, I didn't know you had company.

BUSINESSMAN: It's all right, Mrs Knower – I'm just leaving. You have a clever husband – take good care of him.

[BUSINESSMAN *exits*]

MRS KNOWER: Take care of him! It's a wonder I ever see him, the time he spends out here! Look, I can't have this bale of hay cluttering up the kitchen any longer. [*She puts it down*] And when the animals arrive, they mustn't enter the house. I've enough to do as it is, what with all this dirt and dust. It's weeks since I've had the place spotless. Ever since you had your dream, I've been sweeping up and polishing every day, but it does no good.

KNOWER: I'm sorry. I know it has been rather a strain. But remember – it's not my doing: this is the will of Alpha!

MRS KNOWER: Then I wish He'd planned it to be less mucky! I can hardly turn round for packing cases, provisions, bags of animal food . . .

KNOWER: It won't be for much longer. [*He kisses her forehead*] You're a good wife to me. Not many women would be as patient as you.

MRS KNOWER: More fool me! I'm too soft, that's my trouble.

KNOWER: You're kindhearted, and I wouldn't change you one little bit.

MRS KNOWER: There! Now I don't know what to say! I came out here to moan at you, and now you've put me in a right tizzy. You always get your own way, Benjamin Knower – I never seem to win! I hope Alpha realizes that – otherwise He might be in for a nasty shock!

[*Enter* PHILLIP, *an elderly friend*]

Ah, Phillip –

PHILLIP: Hello, Martha.

MRS KNOWER: [*She takes* PHILLIP *aside*] Try to talk some sense into him. He's spent all our savings on supplies of food and I can hardly move indoors without tripping over some package or other. If it's not for us, it's for the animals.

[MRS KNOWER *exits*]

PHILLIP: Animals? You're not planning to take animals in that thing, are you?

KNOWER: That was the general idea. I haven't spread it around yet, though.

PHILLIP: I should think not! You've made yourself look silly enough already with your fantastic dream! It's given some people around here the best laugh they've had in years. Honestly, Benjamin – don't you think you're carrying the whole idea too far?

KNOWER: I can't agree.

PHILLIP: Well, that's up to you, of course. But most people have sense enough these days to believe in themselves, in living for enjoyment, in life for life's sake – as I thought you did, until you had this nightmare . . .!

KNOWER: It wasn't a nightmare.

PHILLIP: It must have been to change you like this! Floods indeed! The whole of civilization wiped out! Huh!

KNOWER: You don't understand. Take a look at our society and its values, see how precariously we exist between war and peace. Ask yourself whether Mankind is worthy to go on.

PHILLIP: But we must go on – you can't stop progress.

KNOWER: No – it's time we called a halt. When the very air we breathe – when life itself is polluted – when the world is dying beneath a suffocating wreath of chemical waste and diesel fumes – when there are nothing but motorway jungles, treeless cities, plastic garbage . . .

PHILLIP: Benjamin, you're wrong! I know you are!

KNOWER: Then you must think Alpha is wrong too.

PHILLIP: If Alpha *has* spoken to you! For all you know, it's just your imagination – or something you've eaten for supper. You think you know all the answers!

KNOWER: I've none of the answers. I'm just an old man who does as he's told and then sits back and waits.

PHILLIP: And supposing you go on waiting, and waiting – and nothing happens? What then?

KNOWER: Well, Alpha can change His mind. It says in the old Bible that He moves in a mysterious way . . .

PHILLIP: You'll be a laughing stock! Like those fanatics who preach the end of the world – and then die at home in their warm beds!

KNOWER: I hope you're right. That way, there will be no second flood. Alpha will have found it possible to forgive us and let us continue. Nothing would please me more than to know that the world will go on spinning, and that night and day will follow each other as they do now.

PHILLIP: It's useless talking to you. You won't listen to reason. It's commonsense: there won't be any flood! What, here in the middle of England?

KNOWER: This time it needn't be a flood. It may be some other form of disaster.

PHILLIP: [*Rising*] I'd best leave you to your hammering, before I say something I'll regret.

KNOWER: You have been a good friend, Phillip. I pray to Alpha that you'll believe me before it's too late.

PHILLIP: Alpha? Huh! Who believes in Him these days . . .!

[PHILLIP *exits.* SIMON, KNOWER'*s youngest son, enters*]

KNOWER: Who indeed . . .? [*Sadly*] Who indeed . . .? [*He resumes his hammering*]

SIMON: Want any help, Dad?

KNOWER: No, I think I can manage. Tell me, Simon, do you think I'm crazy?

SIMON: Of course not! And even if I did, I wouldn't say so. You're my dad. I'd punch anyone who took the mickey out of you.

KNOWER: All this . . . all this, it's just a game, isn't it?

SIMON: Not a game. An adventure! Something I've never felt so happy about before in my whole life. My dad is making history . . .

KNOWER: Unfortunately, if my dream comes true, we shall *be* history. It will all have to begin again, with us.

SIMON: Somewhere out there, somewhere on another planet?

KNOWER: In another galaxy, perhaps.

SIMON: But how will we survive? How will you know where to go?

KNOWER: Alpha will guide us.

SIMON: What – through the universe?

KNOWER: Yes, in search of a new life. Does it frighten you?

SIMON: I expect I'll miss my friends and television and things like that – but think of it! It's like a dream – I can hardly imagine it's true . . .

[*Song* – Through Space We Shall Travel – *sung by* SIMON]

1. Through space we shall travel
In search of a star,
A new world to found on
Some planet afar;
Speck in a universe,
Fragment of life –
All that remains of
A world torn by strife.

Chorus
This world grows dim and earth is our home no more,
We journey on where no man has been before;

Destin'd to roam, the space maze we shall explore
In our tiny spinning cannister
We grope – we grope for a dream . . .

2. As tense and uncertain
What fate holds in store,
Comets flash by us
And time is no more;
Swallow'd in silence and
Sailing alone
Uncharter'd wastelands
In search of a home.

Chorus

KNOWER: A dream . . .

[*Enter* PETER, *another son, and* RUTH, *his wife. Both look tired.* PETER *carries some sheets of paper*]

PETER: We've searched through half the zoos in England and we still can't come up with more than a third of the animals on this list.

RUTH: Honestly, it's worse than going to the supermarket on a Saturday morning.

KNOWER: Have you brought them all with you?

PETER: John and Mary are just driving the lorries up now. We won't unload them until you're ready.

RUTH: We've risked life and limb for you!

KNOWER: I'm glad the keepers co-operated.

PETER: Co-operated? You must be joking! You don't think we asked their permission?

SIMON: How did you get them out, then?

PETER: Well, we hid in the zoos till after closing time. Then I picked the locks on the cages with some wire.

SIMON: Wow – weren't you frightened?

PETER: I must admit the animals seemed happy to get away . . .!

KNOWER: Ah, good.

PETER: But not so happy about coming here.

RUTH: No, Peter and I had one hell of a job getting them into the lorries.

KNOWER: But didn't you try coaxing them in?

PETER: By holding a carrot in front of the donkey's nose? No, we were worried about the meat-eaters mixing with the vegetarians.

KNOWER: You needn't have worried. They won't fight each other. They didn't in the ark.

RUTH: In the ark, no. In the lorries, yes!

PETER: I'm afraid we've lost a couple of deer.

KNOWER: Not a very good beginning . . .

PETER: And I'm afraid there are three lions.

KNOWER: Three? I only wanted two!

PETER: We couldn't leave an odd one behind.

KNOWER: No, no. Dear me – I hope we can get three lions in . . . [*He spreads out his plans*] I haven't made provision for three . . .

PETER: And don't ask us to go out again tomorrow, dad. Once bitten, twice shy!

KNOWER: That won't be necessary. My dream said the ship must be ready by today.

PETER: Today!

RUTH: Have you told mum?

KNOWER: No. You three had better run along and see she has everything ready.

PETER: You mean that contraption is finished? You've nothing else to do?

KNOWER: Nothing – except pray that it will work all right!

[PETER, SIMON *and* RUTH *exit.* KNOWER *goes on working, then disappears from sight behind the rocket. Slowly, some animals enter, unseen by* KNOWER, *and look around them, bewildered*]

FIRST MONKEY: It's a good job we're out of that zoo. Those bars were confoundedly draughty.

FIRST ELEPHANT: Mind you, I didn't have a chance to wash myself, or pack anything in my trunk to eat on the journey.

SECOND ELEPHANT: Never mind.

FIRST SHEEP: How clever of foxie to get us out of those horrid lorries.

SECOND SHEEP: But won't the humans be annoyed when they find out?

FIRST SHEEP: It's their own silly faults for leaving us shut up like that.

COW: But why have they brought us here?

FIRST SHEEP: Pythie said they plan to experiment on us, like the Americans. We're to be sent into space.

FIRST ELEPHANT: Nonsense, I'd never get off the ground.

SECOND MONKEY: Anyway, you don't want to believe that old snake-in-the-grass; he's just a troublemaker!

SNAKE: It's all right for you monkeys, but someone has to be a snake! Just because I hiss at you all the time, it doesn't mean to say I enjoy being unpleasant.

SECOND ELEPHANT: If you ask me – snakes are just a bunch of crawlers!

SNAKE: That's what most people think. Ever since the Garden of Eden, no one has trusted us. Sometimes I wish I had been born a dog.

DOG: Well, it's not all fun being man's best friend, either. You don't know what hard work it is! I have to do the most appalling things for a chocolate drop – stand on my hind legs and twist around! It's so humiliating!

FIRST ELEPHANT: It's the same with us. They feed buns to us all day. Nasty sticky buns. I can't stand them!

SECOND ELEPHANT: They have all sorts of stupid ideas – but to send us up into space! I don't believe they'd be as dotty as that!

SECOND SHEEP: But it's true, isn't it, Bruno?

BEAR: Yes. Do you remember the stories our parents told about a great flood and a floating wooden ship?

LION: The ark, you mean?

FOX: That's it! Well, it's all going to happen again. The humans who brought us in the lorries said so – we heard them!

SECOND SHEEP: Oooh – and I get so sea-sick!

FIRST MONKEY: But I don't see any wooden ship . . .

BEAR: It's to be a rocket this time, isn't it, Foxie? To take us to another world.

LION: I don't think I'd like that. The Union of Animals will have something to say about it, I'm sure. Is there a shop steward among us?

FIRST PENGUIN: Yes, brothers.

SECOND PENGUIN: Me, too.

LION: Then we'll listen to them and see what they decide.

FIRST PENGUIN: It appears this object is the spaceship.

SECOND PENGUIN: And just look at it – there doesn't seem to be much room!

FIRST ELEPHANT: I couldn't turn round in that thing, even though I'm only a baby!

SHEEP: Quite right!

LION: Travel in that! It's unthinkable!

[*Song* – It's a Dog's Life – *sung by the* ANIMALS]

Chorus

It's a dog's life being an animal!
They monkey around as they please!
From today to the time of Hannibal,
They hunt and they taunt and they tease! (repeat)

1. It's worse than a zoo,
We'll all go cuckoo
Just shut up together;
The parrot will jaw,
The donkey hee-haw,
We're not birds of a feather!
Oh, what are humans coming to?
Why do they treat us so?
They have civil rights for themselves, but when
It's us they don't want to know!

Chorus

2. It will be for sure
A most awful bore,
Having to be friendly;
The cow will go moo,
The skunk will still pooh!
It's certain that in the end we
Will hate each other even more,
Before we reach that star;
We're treated like sheep, and so
Just hear the way we say BAA!

Chorus

FIRST MONKEY: What do you suggest then, brothers?
FIRST PENGUIN: You want us to decide?
FIRST SHEEP: Yes, and then we'll follow you. We're used to doing that!
SECOND PENGUIN: We'll have to confer a moment. [*They confer*]
FOX: Certainly. We're in no hurry.
FIRST ELEPHANT: We've nowhere to go in particular.
LION: And we're certainly not going up!

FIRST PENGUIN: Brothers – and sisters. We are unanimously of the opinion that to be sent up in that thing is quite ludicrous!

ALL: Hear, hear!

FIRST PENGUIN: So, we must refuse to move. A sit-down strike, brothers – a sit-down strike!

[*All the* ANIMALS *sit silently.* KNOWER *re-appears and sees them*]

KNOWER: Good grief! They've been let out before I'm ready for them. Oh dear, it makes the place so crowded.

[KNOWER *works on his rocket. The* THREE FEMALE NEIGHBOURS *re-enter, with moveable fencing. They stand behind the fence*]

FIRST NEIGHBOUR: Would you believe it! An elephant in his back garden! And some lions!

SECOND NEIGHBOUR: Nasty things, lions. The things Mrs Knower has to put up with!

THIRD NEIGHBOUR: I mean, it lowers the tone of the neighbourhood.

FIRST NEIGHBOUR: And gardens weren't designed to be Safari Parks! As soon as I saw them there, I got straight on the 'phone to the R.S.P.C.A.

SECOND NEIGHBOUR: You didn't!

FIRST NEIGHBOUR: I did. I mean, it's not natural. All those animals, stuck out there in that garden. Mark my words, they'll soon sort him out!

[*The* THREE NEIGHBOURS *exit with fencing, as the* R.S.P.C.A. OFFICIAL *enters. He carries a briefcase and has a bowler hat. He looks around at the animals*]

R.S.P.C.A. OFFICIAL: Well, well, well – quite a collection you have here, Mr – ?

KNOWER: Knower. I beg your pardon, I didn't see you.

R.S.P.C.A. OFFICIAL: No wonder, what with all these in the way. I'm from the R.S.P.C.A. and naturally I'm concerned about their welfare. What are you planning to do with them?

KNOWER: I'm taking them on a journey.

R.S.P.C.A. OFFICIAL: A journey? H'mm . . . are you leaving the country?

KNOWER: Yes – in a manner of speaking.

R.S.P.C.A. OFFICIAL: Ah, then you'll have read all the regulations concerning the transportation of animals. Tell me, have they been inoculated?

KNOWER: Inoculated?

R.S.P.C.A. OFFICIAL: Yes. I'm not letting any of these animals leave here unless they've been properly inoculated.

KNOWER: Well – I didn't think it would be necessary . . .

R.S.P.C.A. OFFICIAL: I take it you know the quarantine regulations?

KNOWER: Er, quarantine?

R.S.P.C.A. OFFICIAL: Hells bells, man! Don't tell me you haven't done a thing!

KNOWER: Well – there was nothing about regulations in my dream.

R.S.P.C.A. OFFICIAL: Dream? Dream! This is reality, Mr Knower – the twentieth century! You can't do anything without rules and regulations.

[MINISTRY OF WORKS OFFICIAL *enters, bowler-hatted and carrying briefcase.*]

WORKS OFFICIAL: Good morning.

KNOWER: Good morning.

WORKS OFFICIAL: Mr Knower?

KNOWER: Yes?

WORKS OFFICIAL: I'm from the Ministry of Works. It's about this construction you're building in the garden.

KNOWER: It's built, actually . . .

WORKS OFFICIAL: Built? Built, is it? Well, we can't recall giving any planning permission.

KNOWER: Planning permission?

WORKS OFFICIAL: We've searched and searched, but there aren't any papers in your name.

KNOWER: But I didn't think I needed planning permission.

WORKS OFFICIAL: Not need it? Come, come! For a thing that size! It's interfering with television reception around here for a start. It'll have to come down.

KNOWER: Come down?

WORKS OFFICIAL: Yes, I'm very sorry, but there it is. It should never have gone up in the first place.

[MINISTRY OF AVIATION *and* CUSTOMS AND EXCISE OFFICIALS *enter, with briefcases and bowlers*]

AVIATION OFFICIAL: Good morning!

KNOWER: Good morning.

AVIATION OFFICIAL: Ministry of Aviation.

CUSTOMS OFFICIAL: Customs and Excise.

AVIATION OFFICIAL: Mr Knower, we hear from some neighbours that you are planning to go on a journey, but you haven't complied with a single rule or regulation.

CUSTOMS OFFICIAL: That's very naughty, you know!

KNOWER: [*Exasperated*] Rules and regulations? But I'm trying to save the human race from total destruction.

CUSTOMS OFFICIAL: Now, now, Mr Knower – that's no excuse!

[*Song* – For Sure There's a Law Against It – *sung by the* FOUR OFFICIALS]

Chorus

If there's something you may want to do
For sure there's a law against it!

Though we may look fools
We have reams of rules,
Ancient laws with obscure clause,
Forms galore to stack and store;
Questionnaires to add to your cares,
Sheets to sign on the dotted line –
Documents that don't make sense!
Red tape! Blue tape!
Orange tape! Yellow tape!
If you don't want it –
We've got it!

WORKS: It's the law, are you sure
You really want to fly this?
AVIATION: You're a pilot? No?
You really cannot try this!

Chorus
If you have a plan in Hindustan,
For sure there's a law against it!
Though we may look fools
We have reams of rules [*Etc., as above*]

R.S.P.C.A.: Is it true, they say you
Are taking others in it?
CUSTOMS: You've a passport? No?
You really can't begin it!

Chorus
If you hope to save folk from the grave,
For sure there's a law against it!
Though we may look fools
We have reams of rules [*Etc., as above*]

[*They shower* KNOWER *with forms*]

KNOWER: Forms! Why must there always be forms?

WORKS OFFICIAL: People need work, Mr Knower – surely you wouldn't deprive them of that!

AVIATION OFFICIAL: Just because you see everything so cut and dried, life isn't all that simple!

R.S.P.C.A. OFFICIAL: Well, Mr Knower, I think we've made ourselves plain. This rocket stays here.

WORKS OFFICIAL: Oh no, it comes down!

CUSTOMS OFFICIAL: I think it should stay here.

WORKS OFFICIAL: I'm sorry, but it must be dismantled forthwith.

AVIATION OFFICIAL: Well, it certainly can't go up.

WORKS OFFICIAL: Ah, there we're agreed.

CUSTOMS OFFICIAL: And no goods must be taken out of the country without customs clearance.

KNOWER: [*Sadly*] If I haven't got my rocket, that won't apply.

CUSTOMS OFFICIAL: Good – so long as I've made myself clear.

R.S.P.C.A. OFFICIAL: And what's more, Mr Knower, while these animals are in your back garden, they are to be properly fed and cared for – at *your* expense.

[*The* BUSINESSMAN *re-enters, carrying several newspapers*]

BUSINESSMAN: Having trouble, Mr Knower?

KNOWER: That's an understatement. It appears I am earthbound. These gentlemen refuse to let my ship leave.

BUSINESSMAN: I might have guessed. You're no businessman, Mr Knower, that's your trouble. I thought so all along. A keen brain, but not 'au fait' with the world at large.

KNOWER: All my hard work seems to have been wasted.

BUSINESSMAN: Not wasted – misused. And misappropriated by your humble servant here. I expect you know by now. I've interested all the world's major package tour companies in this little project. We've had advertisements in every newspaper across the world. No half measures for this venture – there's big money in it, boy, big money!

KNOWER: What venture? I don't know what you are talking about.

BUSINESSMAN: Still so naïve, Knower, old fellow? Dear, dear! Never mind! Why do you think I've been so interested in your rocket? You didn't think I had faith in your dream, did you? No, I know a money spinner when I see one! I've noted every screw, every detail in your design. It's brilliant! An inspiration! You know, you really should have had it patented.

KNOWER: Patented?

BUSINESSMAN: Yes, but it's too late for that now. I've had it patented myself. No business head – that's been your trouble all along.

KNOWER: I'm still not completely clear . . .

BUSINESSMAN: Rockets, old friend, rockets! Thousands of them, built to my – or rather, your – specification, all over the world! It's a new boon for the tour companies – everyone's clamouring to get on the band wagon. They're all fed up with work, with people telling them what to do – they want to have a rest for the remainder of their lives. So we're offering them the chance on one of our extended holiday rocket trips. I wonder you haven't booked your seat? Of course, it is a bit of a cheek on one of your own rockets – but that's life, Knower old fellow, that's life!

KNOWER: I still don't understand. Do you mean to say that you're leaving and I'm not?

BUSINESSMAN: That's it, old boy! You've hit the nail on the head! I knew you'd get there sometime. Of course, we're not taking the animals. Sanitation difficulties, you know, not healthy. And anyway, it leaves more room to cram in the customers.

KNOWER: Customers? But if you're selling this 'holiday' – think of the expense . . .!

BUSINESSMAN: As much down as they can afford, and all their

belongings mortgaged for life! I tell you, we're making a bomb! The whole world is getting ready to leave – hospital ships, pensioners' rockets – you name it, we've thought of it! And all the regulations complied with – every form filled in, everything Ministry approved.

KNOWER: I don't believe it. How did you succeed where I failed?

BUSINESSMAN: You've got to sell it to them, old friend – otherwise they don't want to know. [*To the* OFFICIALS] I wonder you gentlemen aren't clamouring to get your tickets. The queue in London half an hour ago was ten miles long. But seeing that you are Ministry officials, I *could* manage to slip you in on an early flight. The first ones leave on Friday. Come along now – don't look so pensive . . .

[*Song* – The Voyage of a Lifetime – *sung by the* BUSINESSMAN, OFFICIALS *and* NEIGHBOURS *who re-enter and crowd round to read the newspaper headlines*]

Chorus

The Voyage of a Lifetime is coming your way!
Go hang the expense, you've a lifetime to pay!
Demand is enormous – book your seat today!
On the Voyage of . . . on the Voyage of . . .
On the Voyage of a Lifetime,
A new world away . . . a new world away . . . a new world away . . .

1. Package tours are just old hat,
   Cyprus, Greece – forget all that!
   Let your hair down,
   Have a ball!
   Hang on chum – bang the drum –
   And then join us one and all!

   Chorus

2. Got a feeling in my bones,

Have a rave-up, end your moans!
Twist and gyrate,
Shriek and yell!
End the drag – Pack your bag
For a psychedelic hell!

Chorus

[*As the song fades, the* NEIGHBOURS, OFFICIALS, PHILLIP *and the* BUSINESSMAN *exit, talking excitedly.* KNOWER *sits, his head lowered,* PETER, SIMON *and* RUTH *enter again*]

PETER: What did they want?

KNOWER: It's all over, son – the dream has faded.

[MRS KNOWER *enters with bundles, followed by* JOHN *and* MARY]

MRS KNOWER: Benjamin, why didn't you tell me we were leaving today? I've made an appointment to have my hair done tomorrow – it's such a waste. I've cut a few sandwiches for the journey. I hope there'll be enough. Mary, bring that bag of monkey nuts out, we may as well start loading.

KNOWER: [*Rising*] Wife, I'm afraid – Oh, you tell her, Ruth . . .

RUTH: I think we're not leaving after all, mum.

MRS KNOWER: [*Furious*] Not leaving! What! After putting up with the mess and banging all these weeks! Look at that animal, it's sitting on my rockery! Shooo!! And what about these sandwiches? The bread will go dry if they're not eaten. [*Looks upwards*] I shall have a few words to say to Alpha about this! Not leaving, indeed!

JOHN: But why this sudden change of heart, dad? What's happened?

KNOWER: No change of heart, John. I'm afraid officialdom has reared its ugly head, that's all. They won't allow me to fly my ship. So many rules and regulations! So, we are to stay here and it's the others who are leaving.

MARY: The others, Mr Knower?

KNOWER: Yes, everyone is booking for the voyage of a lifetime in rockets built to the design Alpha gave me in my dream!

MARY: So we won't be rushing off after all.

MRS KNOWER: Good. I can keep that appointment at the hairdresser's.

KNOWER: If he's still there to see you. Work and responsibility are the things people are trying to escape.

PETER: And Alpha's given them the opportunity through this rocket of His! How ironic – there will be no flood after all, just a mass exit!

RUTH: No disaster, no great catastrophe . . .

JOHN: And no one else, just us, left on this planet with the animals and the seas and the forests . . .

SIMON: Maybe we shall have to begin again after all . . .

KNOWER: [*Thoughtfully*] Maybe we shall. [*Looks up, arms outstretched*] I wonder . . . Alpha . . .? Is *this* the Promised Land . . .?

[*Lights fade. Slow curtain. Reprise* – The Voyage of a Lifetime – *sung during curtain-call*]

Island

Michael Barwis

Cast

LINDA
PENNY
JIMMY
POLICEMAN
A VERY BIG JUGGERNAUT
OTHER JUGGERNAUTS
B.B.C. MAN
FIREMAN
MOTHER
GENERAL
MERCURY
NIGEL
SOLDIER
GIRL
ARAB
SOLDIERS, FIREMEN, CROWDS

Island

SCENE: Traffic island with traffic light and two bollards. Light facing audience. The whole does not need to be completely realistic. The stage kept bright to denote daylight except where indicated. A tape of traffic noises, car engines, hootings, brakes etc., to be used as directed. The lights are at present at red.

Two girls, sisters, PENNY *and* LINDA, *aged 13 and 14, come on pushing bicycles.*

LINDA: Come on, Penny. Before the lights change.

[*They look up at light just as it changes to green. A burst of traffic noise, loud and continuous. They stand ready poised to cross, turning their heads in unison as traffic crosses. Traffic noise fades to background*]

PENNY: [*Impatient*] Oh, come on. Come on. Change.
LINDA: I can't see him. Oh, hurry up.
PENNY: Look. There's a gap. Come on.

[*Makes to go forward, squeal of brakes*]

LINDA: [*Screams*] Mind out, Penny . . . Oh, you frightened me.
PENNY: [*Jumps back, pokes her tongue out at passing car*] Moo to you too. Think you're everybody just because you've got a Rolls Royce. Silly old fool.

LINDA: Coo, that was a near one. [*Looks over shoulder*] I can't see him. Oh, [*To lights*] hurry up.

PENNY: We wouldn't half cop it if mum knew.

LINDA: Well, she doesn't. And besides I don't see why we should have to take him along with us whenever we go out. It isn't fair. Who'd have a younger brother?

PENNY: He's old enough to play on his own.

LINDA: I know . . . It'd be different if he was a baby in a pram. Oh, hurry up and change.

[*Pushes bike wheel forward and pulls it back quickly at burst of traffic noise*]

PENNY: Do you think the lights have stuck?

[*Traffic noise rises and fades*]

LINDA: Oh, blow. He's seen us.

JIMMY: [*Off – calling*] Linda. Penny. Wait for me.

LINDA: Pretend you haven't seen him.

PENNY: I bet the little sneak will tell Mum.

LINDA: He'd better not. I'll tell on him for pinching those doughnuts. Oh, come on, change, change, change.

[*The lights change from green to red. Traffic noise loud with sudden violent squeal of brakes. Noise stops. Linda starts across, sees* PENNY *is looking back off stage*]

Penny, come on. Hurry.

[*They set off with bikes. Before they reach the island,* JIMMY *comes on. He is eleven, is also riding bike. He has a large satchel on his back. He misses his footing on the pedals and propels himself using his feet, his satchel swings round and gets in his way, he stops, slings it over his shoulder in middle of road and starts off again*]

PENNY: Jimmy! Go back. Go back. You'll be run over.

JIMMY: I shan't.
PENNY: All right then. Get run over. See if we care.
LINDA: Oh, come on, Penny. The lights'll change.

[JIMMY *on island, tangles with* PENNY*'s bike. They try to free themselves. Get involved with* LINDA*'s bike*]

PENNY: Now look what you've done.

[*They end up in a heap.*]

LINDA: You clumsy idiot.
JIMMY: Clumsy yourself.
LINDA: [*Freeing herself and bike*] We'll miss the lights if you don't hurry. Leave him there, Penny. Quick. [*But the lights change to green*] Oh, it's too late.

[*Roar of traffic, gear changing etc. They are marooned. Shout at each other but noise drowns their voices as they argue. Sound fades*]

JIMMY: [*Shouting*] Anyhow, why shouldn't I come?
LINDA: Because we don't want you.
PENNY: Why don't you go and play in the park? Go and climb a tree or something.
JIMMY: I don't want to. Besides, I've climbed one.
LINDA: It's a pity you didn't fall and break your neck.
JIMMY: Anyhow, where are you going?
LINDA: Where small boys aren't wanted.
JIMMY: [*Mimicking*] Oh. Where small boys aren't wanted. [*He pokes his tongue out*]
PENNY: Oh, I suppose he'll have to come now.
LINDA: Let's let his tyres down. Then he won't be able to.
JIMMY: You needn't bother. I don't want to come. Not with silly girls.
LINDA: I wish those lights would change.

[*Leans over and bangs the lamp post. Nothing happens. The girls turn their heads in unison as traffic passes. Noise up.* JIMMY *calmly props his bike against bollard, unslings satchel. Noise down*]

PENNY: What d'you think you're doing?
JIMMY: [*Casually*] Nothing.
LINDA: Oh, well, stay there if that's what you want.

[*Gets ready to cross but traffic continues*]

Come on, Penny. Get ready. The lights'll change soon.
JIMMY: You'll have a long time to wait.
PENNY: What d'you mean?
JIMMY: They aren't going to change.
PENNY: Don't be silly. Of course they will.
JIMMY: They won't.
PENNY: [*Doubtfully*] How do you know?
JIMMY: Oh, I just know. We're on a desert island.
LINDA: Don't be daft.
JIMMY: You'll see. [*Traffic noise up and extends.* JIMMY *forages in his satchel. Noise down*] There you are. We're shipwrecked mariners. I told you so.
LINDA: And I'll tell you something, you silly little fool . . . What are you doing?

[JIMMY *has taken a telescope from his satchel, climbs lamp standard, puts telescope to his eye and peers round*]

Jimmy, come down at once. [*He takes no notice*] What d'you think you're up to?
JIMMY: I'm on Spyglass Hill. Looking for enemies.
LINDA: He's gone mad. Oh, come, leave him there.

[*She pushes bike forward,* PENNY *follows, violent traffic noise, squeal of brakes, they retreat hurriedly*]

JIMMY: Ya, I told you so.
LINDA: Ya, look at him, monkey up a tree.
PENNY: Come down. This minute. You might be killed . . . Oh well, stay there, then. [*She turns to traffic, waiting to cross*]
LINDA: [*Doubtfully*] Penny, what if he's right? It doesn't look as though the lights will ever change.

[JIMMY, *while the girls are watching the traffic, has come down, goes to satchel, takes out rope, runs round* GIRLS *and encircles them with it*]

LINDA: What are you doing? Stop it, Jimmy.
PENNY: Stop it, I tell you. What are you playing at?
JIMMY: I told you. Desert islands. You're traitors.
LINDA: Let me go.
PENNY: Jimmy, do what you're told!
LINDA: You wait. I'll tell mum of you when we get home.
JIMMY: We won't get home. We're here for ever.
PENNY: What d'you mean?
JIMMY: We're marooned. Jolly good fun too.
LINDA: Jimmy, don't be silly.

[JIMMY *takes fur hat and bush-ranger-type coat from satchel. Attached to shoulder of coat when he puts it on is a green parrot – stuffed – he also takes out a wooden gun which he slings over his shoulder*]

PENNY: [*To* LINDA] Do you think it's true? Shan't we get away?
LINDA: [*Looking at traffic – gloomily*] It doesn't look like it . . . Oh, Jimmy, undo us.
JIMMY: Who's the King of the Island?

[GIRLS *hesitate, look at each other*]

PENNY: He means it.
JIMMY: Come on, who's the King of the Island?

PENNY: You are.
JIMMY: Do you swear to obey?
LINDA: Oh yes, yes. But hurry up and set us free.
JIMMY: I'll think about it.

[JIMMY *is in no hurry. He takes a sandwich from satchel and begins to eat it*]

PENNY: Give us a bite.
LINDA: We're hungry too.
JIMMY: Too late. It's the last one. [*He undoes rope*] And don't forget. I'm the King.

[*He climbs standard with telescope. Stares across. A* POLICEMAN *appears at side. Puts hand up sailor fashion to his eyes, peering at island, moving head from side to side in attempt to see between traffic, hopping from one foot to other in exaggerated manner*]

JIMMY: Enemy approaching from the West. Prepare to defend the island.
LINDA: Where? Where?

[*They see* POLICEMAN]

PENNY: Hooray. We shall be rescued!

[*Both wave arms vigorously*]

[*Traffic noise up.* POLICEMAN *launches himself towards them, dancing about, dodging, retreating, blows his whistle, shouts at cars etc., is driven back and recommences his miming. At last arrives on island on hands and knees, is dragged up by* GIRLS. *Pulls himself together. Straightens his hat and tunic. Traffic noise down*]

POLICEMAN: Now then, now then. What's all this 'ere?
PENNY: Please sir, we're marooned. We can't get away.

POLICEMAN: [*Sees* JIMMY] Hm. Masquerading in a public place. I must ask you for your name and address.

JIMMY: Robinson Crusoe, Spy Glass Hill, Treasure Island. Who are you? Man Friday?

POLICEMAN: No, I'm not.

JIMMY: Yes, you are. [*Gets out large magnifying glass*] There's your footprints. Size twelve.

POLICEMAN: Now then, that's enough of that. [*Tilts helmet, scratches head, meditating*]

LINDA: Oh please, try and get us off.

POLICEMAN: Ah. Well. We'll have to see about that. Just you leave it to me. I'll soon have this lot sorted out.

PENNY: What are you going to do?

POLICEMAN: I shall invoke the majesty of the law. Section 16, subsection 24, para. 82 Police Traffic Regulations.

PENNY: Oh, do be careful, Mr Policeman.

JIMMY: You'll be eaten by sharks. And whales.

POLICEMAN: [*Blows whistle. Fearful squealing of brakes, honking, traffic noise loud. He slips off island, spins round*] Help . . .

[*Is pulled back by* JIMMY. *He mops his brow. Noise down*]

PENNY: Are you all right?

POLICEMAN: [*Nods*] Phew . . . Well, there's nothing for it. I'll have to call up the police station. [*Takes out his pocket radio*] P.C. Jonah reporting. I am on traffic island 483. Calling all cars. Emergency. Operation Rescue. Over and out. [*Listens. Traffic noise up and down. Shakes head*] It's no good. They can't hear me. Hm. Now what do we do?

PENNY: It must be tea time. I'm hungry.

LINDA: We shall starve to death. There isn't anything left to eat.

JIMMY: Oh yes, there is. [*Shakes lamp standard. Three bananas fall down. Scramble to get them,* POLICEMAN *joining in.*] One of them is mine.

LINDA: No it isn't. You've had a sandwich.

[*She has picked up two bananas. She ceremoniously hands one to* POLICEMAN *who bows, accepts it.*]

POLICEMAN: Are you trying to bribe me, young lady? Thank you very much.

[PENNY *has other banana. They solemnly eat them while* JIMMY *dances around trying to get a bite and failing.* POLICEMAN *collects skins*]

POLICEMAN: What, no litter bin? [*Presents skins to* JIMMY *who throws them off furiously.* POLICEMAN *shakes his head disapprovingly*] Tut tut.

LINDA: I'm thirsty.

POLICEMAN: Ah. Well now. [*Takes off helmet, bales up from edge of island, hands it to* LINDA. *She goes to drink, screams, spits it out*]

LINDA: Ow, it's petrol. [POLICEMAN *and* GIRLS *smell*]

JIMMY: The seas round the island are polluted. Oil slick, you know.

POLICEMAN: [*Puts helmet on*] I'll try again. [*Puts radio to ear. Shakes head. Blows whistle – traffic noise up then down*]

GIRLS: [*Sadly*] No?

POLICEMAN: No.

PENNY: What are we going to do?

JIMMY: Cor, you aren't half a rotten lot of shipwrecked mariners. [*Points gun at* POLICEMAN] Hand over your notebook. [POLICEMAN *puts hands above his head*] Come on, quick about it or I shoot.

[POLICEMAN *searches, scratches head, suddenly remembers. Takes helmet off, produces notebook, shaking visibly*]

Now your pencil.

[POLICEMAN *is shaking so much, he is quite a time before he hands over the pencil.* JIMMY *scribbles on pad, tears off sheet of paper, takes parrot from his shoulder, stuffs paper in beak, wags finger at it, then holds it in both hands and throws it into wings in manner of launching a pigeon. They wave farewell to it*]

[*Light changes to cold blue slowly*]

PENNY: Oh, I wish they'd hurry up and rescue us.
LINDA: [*To* JIMMY] It's all your fault. Just you wait until we get home.
PENNY: If we ever get home.
JIMMY: I'll have no mutineers on my island. Mr Man Friday, arrest those men – women. Clap them in irons.
POLICEMAN: I'll have to have the charge in writing.
PENNY: Oh no, please, sir, we'll be good.
POLICEMAN: 'Ullo, 'ullo, there's a dirty black cloud coming up. Take cover.
LINDA: Don't be silly. Where can we shelter?

[POLICEMAN *scratches his head*]

POLICEMAN: Ah, now that's a bit of a poser.
JIMMY: Under that palm tree. It's only a tropical storm.

[*They stand under lamp except for* JIMMY *who ties rope between bollards, goes to his satchel, takes out sheet which he hangs over rope to make a makeshift tent. Meanwhile . . .*]

PENNY: I'm cold.
LINDA: So am I. I'm shivering. It's going to snow.
JIMMY: [*Contemptuous*] You don't have snow on a tropical island.
LINDA: I don't care what sort of island it is. I'm cold, I tell you. I shall catch pneumonia.

PENNY: Me too.

[*Darker – thunder and lightning. Girls scream and huddle*]

POLICEMAN: My name's not Walter for nothing. [*Takes his coat off, bows to* LINDA, *puts coat over her shoulders*] Madam, allow me.

LINDA: Oh, I couldn't deprive you, Sir Walter.

POLICEMAN: Your need is greater than mine. [*Raises his helmet*]

PENNY: What about me? I'm frozen to death.

POLICEMAN: [*Hesitates*] For the honour of the police force, I cannot see a damsel in distress.

[*Takes his trousers off revealing a pair of bright red underpants. Puts trousers round* PENNY'*s shoulders*]

When we're rescued, I shall be made a Sergeant for bravery. I might even get the George Medal.

[*Lights fading*]

LINDA: [*Nervously*] It's growing dark. Penny, I'm frightened. What if we have to stay here all night?

PENNY: Oh, I wish we'd never come.

[*Noise up, then down.*]

JIMMY: The wind's getting up. There'll be a hurricane. Batten down the hatches.

LINDA: It's all your fault. I wish I was home in bed.

[*Dark except for green light*]

JIMMY: Friday.

PENNY: Don't be silly. It's only Wednesday.

JIMMY: Man Friday.

POLICEMAN: Was you addressing me?

JIMMY: Yes, I was. I shall stand the first watch. Keep your eyes skinned. There's sea monsters in these waters. And – they come ashore at night.

[*Burst of traffic with honking of horns answered by ditto*]

There they are, calling to each other. They want their supper. They're partial to little girls.

[GIRLS *scream*]

POLICEMAN: D-d-did you say monsters?
JIMMY: Friday.
POLICEMAN: Oh, very well, sergeant . . . I mean, aye, aye, captain.
LINDA: Help, we'll be eaten.
JIMMY: Who'd have women on a desert island? Into the tent with you. [GIRLS *scramble*] And Friday, sing them to sleep.
POLICEMAN: What me? Sing? . . . Oh, all right. [*To* GIRLS] Move along there. Into the tent.

[GIRLS *crawl under awning.* POLICEMAN *sits crosslegged by tent*]

[*Sings to Policeman's Song from* Pirates of Penzance]

When constabulary duty's to be done, to be done,
A traffic copper's job is not much fun, not much fun,
And when stranded in the middle of the High Street, in the High Street,
A policeman's lot is not a happy one. Happy one.

[*The traffic noise becomes rhythmic with a menacing beat, with squeaks and grunts from motor horns etc., quietly at first. Stage almost dark, green traffic light shining. Gradual lurid red flood but still keeping stage subdued.* JIMMY *sits up, hand to ear, listening. Jumps to his feet, comes forward, back to audience, telescope transformed into a wooden sword. He stands on defensive. Rhythm increases – not too loud at present.*

From upstage left a shadowy outline appears – canvas or paper on frame held by actor in front like a shield depicting a cut-out front-view of a JUGGERNAUT *with exaggerated front grill looking like monstrous teeth. If an ultraviolet light is available the headlights and teeth will gleam menacingly.* CAR *advances slowly downstage towards* JIMMY, *accompanied by growls, horn sounds etc.* JIMMY *moves towards it, waving his sword. A mimed battle,* CAR *driven back to corner upstage, snarls etc.* JIMMY *breaks off, moves backwards to downstage centre, stands guard. Three high pitched notes over the rhythmic bass, repeated. Three or four more* JUGGERNAUT *faces come on, advance slowly against* JIMMY *who fights them, using his sword two handed, spinning round etc. The* JUGGERNAUTS *move backwards and forwards as he attacks them but gradually close in on him. Crescendo of noise as they force him downstage. He sinks to his knees as the* JUGGERNAUTS *lean over him. The biggest* JUGGERNAUT, *towering over them all, belches smoke*]

JUGGERNAUT: [*Voice amplified*] Hear me speak. I, the great God Diesel command you. [*Other* JUGGERNAUTS *lurch at* JIMMY] Down on your knees and worship me.

JIMMY: Oh, please, sir, let me go.

JUGGERNAUT: Go? Haw, haw, haw. Where can you go? We juggernauts have taken over the whole world. We are the rulers of the earth. [*Three honking cheers from the others*]

JIMMY: Oh, please, sir, I'll never come on your roads again. I'll go and live in Clapham Common. [*Or some appropriate local park*]

JUGGERNAUT: Haw, haw, haw. There are no commons left. No parks, no fields. We've swallowed them all up.

JIMMY: Oh, please, sir, can I – emigrate across the sea? I've got a passport.

JUGGERNAUT: The sea? Haw, haw. There is no sea. Only lovely oil. Slicks and slicks of it. You'd drown in oil. Ha, ha.

JIMMY: [*Desperate*] Oh. Oh, where can I go?

JUGGERNAUT: Nowhere. You will be offered up to the greater glory of the motorway.

JIMMY: No, no.

JUGGERNAUT: Prepare to be sacrificed on the altar of Progress.

OTHERS: Hail to the great God Diesel.

JIMMY: No. No. I'll – I'll tell my dad of you.

JUGGERNAUT: [*Laughs*] Do you know what we do with dads? and mums? And [*Quicker*] aunts and uncles and cousins and grannies and grandads, and babies – and especially small boys? . . . We pulp them. We chop them up. We tear them apart. We roll on them. We mash them up and feed them to our mini juggernauts so they'll grow up big and strong like us.

JIMMY: [*Jumps up*] No. No. You shan't have me. You shan't.

[*Fights and struggles*]

JUGGERNAUT: [*Great roar*] Finish him. Crush him. Flatten him. Make a jam sandwich of him.

[JUGGERNAUTS *close in on* JIMMY, *leaning over him as he sinks to the ground. A long scream from him*]

[*Black out – Blue light, misty, slowly increases.* JUGGERNAUTS *gone,* JIMMY *back on island. Former traffic noise, as he struggles, waving arms, shouting, wakes up, rubs his eyes, shins up standard with telescope*]

JIMMY: All hands on deck.

[POLICEMAN *jumps to his feet, rubbing his eyes, staggers, nearly falls off island, recovers.* GIRLS *scramble from tent*]

POLICEMAN: [*Still dazed*] Yes, sergeant. No, sergeant. [*Wakes up*]

JIMMY: Man the defences. Enemy approaching from the mainland.

POLICEMAN: Where? Where? [*Looks out on opposite side from where* JIMMY *is looking*]

JIMMY: Not there, you fool.

POLICEMAN: Oh. [*Transfers gaze to other side*] I can't see anything.

JIMMY: We shall fight them on the beaches. [*Comes down standard*] Hoist the red flag.

POLICEMAN: [*Looks down at his red pants. Agonized cry*] No. No. Rather death than dishonour.

[*Runs to side of island, puts hands above head as if about to dive in.* GIRLS *rush to him, drag him back, as traffic noise increases and fades*]

JIMMY: Mr Christian. Will ye disobey me orders? I'll have ye flogged for insubordination.

POLICEMAN: Oh, all right. [*Goes and climbs standard*] Hullo, hullo, a ship in full sail. Coming this way.

LINDA:
PENNY: } [*Together*] Where? Where?

POLICEMAN: [*Points*] There.

[MOTHER *comes on, hair in curlers with chiffon scarf over, trying to see the island between the traffic*]

LINDA:
PENNY: } Cooee, mum. Cooee. [*Wave. Jump up and down*]

[MOTHER *sees them. Shakes her fist. Traffic noise up. She is seen shouting, running back and forward. A lollipop man with lollipop stick comes on.* MOTHER *sees him. Goes up to him. Arguing, waving arms, pointing. Lollipop man shakes head. During this a* B.B.C. REPORTER *with large microphone comes on downstage. Traffic noise down. Lollipop man puts one dainty foot forward, withdraws it hurriedly*]

B.B.C. MAN: We apologize for interrupting Desert Island Discs to bring you an on-the-spot report. The three children marooned on an island on the high seas – I beg your pardon, on the High Street – are still there. Yes. I can see them. They appear alive and well. But it is difficult to catch a glimpse of them. The seas are mountains high. I beg your pardon. The traffic is mountains high. But wait a minute. Yes. Over there. I can see the distracted mother. She seems to be about to do something rash. I mean brave. She is going to cross. [MOTHER *seen struggling with lollipop man, trying to grab his stick*] No. A lollipop man is trying to stop her. Oh, this is terrible. They are struggling. That's what mother love can do for you. She's got hold of his symbol of office. She is stepping off the pavement.

MOTHER: [*Holding stick like a flag*] Excelsior.

[*She steps out, the lollipop stick is torn from her hand, pulled upstage by wire. She staggers back, sinks into the arms of the lollipop man*]

B.B.C. MAN: No. She has failed. The traffic will not stop for her. But listen . . . What do I hear? [*Holds mike out. Sound of fire engine bell and siren in distance, coming closer*] Our gallant firemen. Rescue is at hand.

[FIREMAN *enters running, holding nozzle of fire hose. Followed by three other firemen*]

FIREMAN: Where's the fire? Where's the fire?

[*Runs round in circles until he has wound the hose round the other firemen. While they disentangle themselves*:]

B.B.C. MAN: There appears to be a bit of confusion. No doubt it will sort itself out in a moment. Meanwhile on the island there is excitement at the prospect of an early rescue.

[*On the island the* GIRLS *and* JIMMY *are sitting down elbows on knees, yawning. The* POLICEMAN *appears to have gone to sleep up the lamp standard*]

Oh dear, I'm afraid the firemen are going away again. [*They disentangle themselves and run off*] They must have had a more urgent call. Or [*Laughs*] perhaps they've gone to fetch a plumber. [*Coughs*] I beg your pardon.

[*A flash of light.* MERCURY *runs on, leaping over traffic, unrolls a scroll of parchment in front of* B.B.C. MAN]

Ah, a late news flash . . . [*Reads*] 'Sorry mate, the pigeon post has gone on strike. You needn't tip this fellow, he's on overtime as it is' . . . What? Oh, I beg your pardon. [*Puts finger to parchment, reading*] 'The Minister of Transport has just been speaking in the House of Commons. He states that the Government is considering drastic measures to deal with the situation on the roads. If necessary they will ban all pedestrians from our highways. The country cannot be held to ransom by citizens taking unnecessary journeys on foot. He stresses that the situation is serious but not hopeless. Everything possible is being done.' Well, thank you, Mercury.

[*Another flash.* MERCURY *runs off*]

[*Sound of Col. Bogey march is heard over traffic*]

I can hear something. Yes . . . yes . . . Listen everyone – [*Holds mike up*] it's coming nearer. Everything's going to be all right. The army is on the march. Hooray.

[*Plumed hat* GENERAL *appears riding a prancing hobby horse. He has field glasses round his neck, a loud hailer in one hand. An* OFFICER *runs beside him, stopping every few paces to salute him*]

GENERAL: Now then, Nigel. Where's the enemy?

NIGEL: Well, sir – [*salutes*].

GENERAL: All right, you needn't tell me. I can see for myself. [*Puts glasses to eyes*] Villainous lot they look. Good Lord, there's a naked fuzzy wuzzy. Flying the red flag too. Beastly bolsheviks.

NIGEL: [*Saluting*] But, sir, we've got to rescue –

GENERAL: Don't interrupt, Nigel, old son.

NIGEL: No, sir. [*Salutes*]

GENERAL: We'll soon winkle 'em out.

B.B.C. MAN: [*Approaching*] Excuse me, sir. [NIGEL *salutes*]

GENERAL: Eh? What? Oh, one of those wireless wallahs. Well, what d'ye want?

B.B.C. MAN: Can you tell the listeners, General, what your general strategy is?

GENERAL: Well, it's a general one.

B.B.C. MAN: Thank you, General. But can you elaborate for the listeners?

GENERAL: Simple. Three stages. Get there. Get 'em rounded up. Get out. Back in time for tea.

B.B.C. MAN: Do you anticipate much opposition, sir?

GENERAL: Call the artillery up if we do.

NIGEL: But sir – [*Salutes*]

B.B.C. MAN: But, general, what about the cars and lorries. How will you get there?

GENERAL: What? [*Pointing*] That motorized division? Ha, we'll show 'em what the horses can do, eh? [*Advances. Horse rears*]

NIGEL: Oh, be careful, sir. [*Salutes*]

GENERAL: Don't fuss, Nigel. Now then, you – [*to* B.B.C. MAN] off. Clear the battlefield. [*Turns about, puts loud hailer to mouth*] Advance, men. Take up positions.

[SOLDIERS *run on*]

NIGEL: [*Salutes*] Now, men. Fall in. By the right. Ee [*squeaks*]

[SOLDIERS *shuffle about trying to get into line. They have Cromwellian-type helmets and carry pikes. Comic business of some facing wrong way etc.* NIGEL *squeaking orders. At last* –]

All present and correct, sir. [*Salutes*]

GENERAL: [*Through loud hailer*] Are the artillery ready?

VOICE: [*Off*] Yessir.

GENERAL: Now, lads, we'll soften 'em up with a barrage. Then, when I give the order, you will advance. Over the top and the best of luck.

SOLDIER: Blimey, we'll finish up going to Marble Arch [*or some local landmark*] on the top deck of an 88 bus.

POLICEMAN: Cor, they've got bloomin' great field guns. I didn't join the police force for this.

JIMMY: [*Hand to eyes*] Pirates . . . Take cover. [*They crouch down*]

POLICEMAN: Hi. What about me?

JIMMY: Stay there and draw their fire.

POLICEMAN: Ow. Help?

NIGEL: [*Salutes*] Sir. Sir. [*Salutes*]

GENERAL: [*Not attending*] Not now, Nigel.

NIGEL: But, sir. We've got to rescue them. Not blow them to bits.

GENERAL: What d'ye say? Don't bother me. Can't change me plans . . . [*through hailer*] Gunners. Ready . . . Steady . . . No. No. Cancel that. Gunners . . . One . . . Two . . . Three . . . Fire.

[*Boom of guns. Shells lob towards the island. Loud hooting and honking.* POLICEMAN *slides down lamp standard*]

POLICEMAN: I want a transfer to the St John's Ambulance.

LINDA: [*Picks up shell*] Coo, Penny. Look. It's a Christmas present. Toffees. And toy motor cars. [PENNY *and* LINDA *start eating*] They must be for you, Jimmy.

GENERAL: Hold it, men. Gunners. Reload . . . Prepare to fire. One . . . Two . . . Three . . . Fire.

[*More booms, more shells.* JIMMY *picks up shells, throws them back*]

NIGEL: Oh, sir. [*Salutes*] Please, sir –

GENERAL: Now then, men. [*Tries to pull his sword out. It gets stuck*]

[*A* YOUNG WOMAN *comes on dressed in jeans, sheepskin coat, tassels, highly coloured headscarf etc., and carrying a large banner on which are the words 'KEEP OUR ISLAND CLEAN'. She sidles up to* GENERAL. *Soldiers who have been crouched down ready to advance, straighten up, give wolf whistles, nudge each other*]

GIRL: Naughty, naughty.

GENERAL: Eh? What? What?

GIRL: Oh, shame on you.

GENERAL: Madam, I am doing my duty.

GIRL: But, General, you don't really want to capture that itsy bitsy island, do you?

GENERAL: Madam, I must ask you to retire. There's a war on.

GIRL: But you're fighting the wrong people.

NIGEL: That's what I've been telling the old fool for hours.

GIRL: [*Sidles to him*] Oh, [*lingeringly*] aren't you nice. [*Touches his uniform admiringly*] You don't want to get your beautiful uniform dirty, do you? [*Turns banner, which reads 'MAKE LOVE NOT WAR' on the other side*]

NIGEL: No, I don't.

GENERAL: [*Roaring*] Nigel.

NIGEL: [*Salutes*] Sir.

GENERAL: Put that woman away . . . [*Through hailer*] Men. Get ready.

[GIRL *dodges*]

GIRL: [*Calling across to island*] You stay there, darlings. I'll come and join you when I've dealt with this lot. They want the island for a shooting range.

B.B.C. MAN: Hullo, listeners. Here we are back again . . . Well, I'm afraid there's been a slight hitch.

GIRL: Don't you dare call me a slight hitch. I'm the great British Public and I'm going to stand up for my rights. [*Shouts*] The Country for the People. Down with Pollution. Keep our Island Clean.

B.B.C. MAN: I beg your pardon, Miss. Hullo, hullo, hullo. Here's our frantic mother. She's recovered. She's advancing on the General.

[MOTHER *runs to* GENERAL, *pushes him off his horse, snatches loud hailer. Calls across to island*]

MOTHER: Penny, Linda, Jimmy. Come 'ere. You come back here at once. or I'll give you what for.

JIMMY: We can't. We're shipwrecked.

MOTHER: Don't you answer me back. I'll tell your father.

GENERAL: [*Has remounted his horse*] Nigel. Arrest that woman. Clear the area of civilians.

NIGEL: Sir. [*Salutes*] Excuse me, madam. [*To* MOTHER]

MOTHER: No, I will not. Penny, Linda. Jimmy. Just you wait till I get at you.

NIGEL: Oh dear. [*Snatches loud hailer from her after a struggle*] Pioneer Corps. Ad-vance.

[*Three men run on with shovels, they shoo* MOTHER *out of the way, stand in front of her with shovels at the 'Present Arms'. She tries to see over them.* GIRL *runs towards them*]

GIRL: Down with the Fascist pigs. Women's Liberation for

ever. [*She attacks them.* NIGEL *taps her on shoulder – she turns, flutters her eyelids*] Oh... well, if you insist... [*They go back arm-in-arm*]

GENERAL: Nigel. Where is he? Oh, there you are. Well, don't be long. We're starting the war again, what. [*Turns to* SOLDIERS] Line up men. Weapons at the ready. [*They lower pikes*] When you can see the whites of their headlights, charge. Aim for their tyres.

[*Stands with sword held high. From opposite, the* JUGGERNAUTS *and* CAR FACES *appear. Traffic noise up.* GENERAL *lowers his sword. Charge.* MEN *advance a few steps. Pandemonium breaks out.* JUGGERNAUTS *puff smoke. And smoke from a smoke box spreads over the stage. The* SOLDIERS *are forced back. They collapse in heaps. The* GENERAL *jumps off his horse, runs to lie on stretcher brought on by two* NURSES. *Great roar from* JUGGERNAUTS. *They jump up and down in triumph. The great noise suddenly subsides like a gramophone record running down. Everybody freezes. The* JUGGERNAUTS *stagger. Collapse slowly. Absolute silence. Long pause.* PENNY *and* LINDA *cling together*]

PENNY:
LINDA: } [*Together*] What's happened? What's happened?

JIMMY: [*Suddenly jumps up and down*] Hooray. Hooray.

POLICEMAN: 'Ere, 'ere, what's going on?

JIMMY: [*Shouts*] They've run out of petrol. There's no more petrol left. Whoopee. [*Waves his hat*]

LINDA: Oh, goodie, goodie. We can go. [*Runs to bicycles*]

MOTHER: [*Struggles with* PIONEER MEN] Let me go. I'll teach those little devils a lesson. [*They hold her down*]

[POLICEMAN *runs to space between island and* CROWD. *Stands with arms outstretched. Waves to girls and* JIMMY]

POLICEMAN: Come along. Hurry across. Hurry across.

JIMMY: No fear. We're not going back there. [*Gets his bicycle. Starts packing his satchel*]

GIRL: [*Waving banner*] Don't you, darlings. You hop off and have yourselves a ball.

GENERAL: [*Suddenly jumps up from his stretcher, runs towards island*] Hey, you there. Young man. Ladies. [JIMMY *and* GIRLS *turn*] How much for your bicycles? Look. [*Pulls out sheaf of notes*] Money. Money. I'll pay you anything you want.

[*Great roar from all – they move forward in a body, waving their arms high, their hands full of notes, shouting 'Bicycles, Bicycles'.* FIREMEN *with hose join them. The* POLICEMAN *stands in front of them, arms outstretched, holding them back. As they stop shouting –*]

JIMMY: No fear. You can walk.

LINDA: Come on. [*They all mount their bikes*]

GENERAL: Hi. Wait for me. [*Mounts his horse. They ride off,* GENERAL *waving his sword*] Tally ho.

POLICEMAN: [*Running after them*] Hi. Come back. Stop thief. I want my trousers. [*He runs off after them*]

[*Long sigh from* CROWD *which suddenly freezes as an* ARAB *appears carrying a two-gallon petrol can*]

ARAB: [*Advances to island*] You want petrol? Lovely petrol? [*Roar from* CROWD. *Puts his hand up. Silence*] Very greedy people. You pay much money for my petrol. Teach you lesson. Two hundred pounds a gallon. [*Groan from* CROWD] Very precious. [*Groan from* CROWD] No? Too dear? Ah [*spreads hands*] But Arabs have to live. Same as you. [*Holds petrol can up*] Price up next week. [*Groan*] No buy? [*Groan –* ARAB *turns, walks away, turns*] I very kind hearted man. I sell you instead of petrol, very high class camels. Very fast. Twelve miles an hour. Get you home on a pint of water.

[*Great roar from* CROWD. *They surge forward.* ARAB *walks off, pursued.*

GIRL *and* NIGEL *stand arm in arm. She waves after* CROWD]

George

C. G. Bond

Cast

GEORGE
DAVID
JUDY

George

The action takes place in DAVID *and* JUDY*'s G-Plan living room on a winter's afternoon around five o'clock.* GEORGE*'s cage stands stage centre, and doesn't look as if it belongs there. Neither does* GEORGE*, who is inside it.* GEORGE *is a male Mynah bird with dusty black feathers and eyes that glint. He speaks with the voice of an old woman. His size will be determined by the actor who plays him.*

GEORGE: [*Eyes glint as he takes in the audience, examining them*] Well, well, well, well, well. [*Pause*] What yer doing? [*Puts fingers in beak and gives a piercing whistle*] Well, well, well, well, well.

[*Noise of a Yale key opening a door.* GEORGE *listens intently. Door slams. Footsteps.* DAVID *and* JUDY *enter. They are dressed for the funeral they have just attended.* DAVID *sits – depressed*]

JUDY: Try not to brood, love. It's over.
DAVID: [*Smiling through*] I know.
JUDY: Don't be miserable. She wouldn't want you to be.
DAVID: No. If there is one, she's in it.
JUDY: And you said yourself, she had a jolly good innings.
DAVID: Yes. Seventy-six. Well, it's not a bad age to . . . go, is it? But, oh I don't know . . .

JUDY: What is it, darling?

DAVID: Oh I dunno, I suppose it's inevitable really, you just, well, you just wonder if you couldn't have done more, you know?

JUDY: Oh darling, don't be absurd. I mean . . . gosh, you did everything . . . everything you could, didn't you? I mean, oh don't be silly, darling. You were wonderful with her.

DAVID: [*Removing black tie*] I suppose so. It's just . . . well, it's inevitable I suppose. It just, well, leaves a gap somehow. They don't make 'em like mum any more, you know?

JUDY: I know, darling. Oh, but she was a character wasn't she?

[*They are both lost in fond thoughts*]

DAVID
JUDY } [*Together*] Do you remember . . .

[*They laugh*]

DAVID: So many memories . . .

JUDY: Yes, darling. [*Moves close to him*] So many, many memories.

[*They close their eyes for a kiss, but as their lips meet . . .*]

GEORGE: What yer doing?

[*They turn startled, then laugh.*]

JUDY: And there's George . . .

DAVID: Mm. Dear old George. He's incredible you know. I taught him to whistle. Well, I didn't really teach him, I was whistling one day – it's really incredible this – and he just picked it up. Look, I'll show you. [*Puts fingers in his mouth and whistles.* GEORGE *replies in kind*] You haven't forgotten me then, George boy? [GEORGE *obliges with another whistle*]

JUDY: He's wonderful. How old is he?

DAVID: Oh lord knows. Mum got him for company when dad passed on, but he was fully grown then.

JUDY: What else can he say?

DAVID: I don't really know. I mean, I haven't seen him for ages. [*Quickly*] I mean, I went when I could but, there's so little time, and well, we just didn't seem to, to have much to say to one another after . . . well, as time went on . . .

JUDY: You were marvellous, darling. I know what it cost you. Well . . . [*Pause. Brightly*] Well come on, Georgy-Porgy, surely you must be able to say something else? Eh, Georgy? Georgy-porgy?

DAVID: Oh yes, I know. Well, well, well, well, well.

GEORGE: Well, well, well, well, well.

JUDY: Isn't he . . . aren't you a clever Georgy-Porgy? Aren't you? What else, what else can he say?

DAVID: Um . . . oh, yes. Er . . . give us a kiss, give us a kiss.

[*Accompanied by gestures*]

GEORGE: What yer doing?

DAVID: Oh. No. No, he must have forgotten that one. Um . . . pretty boy, pretty boy.

GEORGE: What yer doing?

DAVID: Oh. Well he used to be able to do all these, I don't er . . .

GEORGE: What yer doing?

JUDY: [*Disappointed*] Oh well, never mind. Is it too early for a sherry?

DAVID: Well . . . no, why not? Good idea. Buck us up a bit.

[*They move away from cage*]

GEORGE: [*Sings. Reedy*]
Oh shepherd of Israel and mine,
The joy and desire of my heart,
For closer communion I pine,
I long to reside where thou art.

[*He whistles.* DAVID *and* JUDY *are transfixed*]

The pastures I languish to find,
Where all who their shepherd obey,
Are fed on they bosom reclined,
And screened from the heat of the day.
[*Softly*] Well, well, well, well, well.

JUDY: But . . .

DAVID: Fantastic, I mean, that is . . . fantastic.

JUDY: But, I mean, I didn't think they could . . .

DAVID: Incredible! She must have taught it to him, well, either that or he just picked it up off her, as she was . . . well, going about. She was always singing, you know, to keep her spirits up.

JUDY: But I didn't think they could learn anything . . . well, as complicated as that.

DAVID: No. I mean neither did I. She must have taught him. Hey, do you think he knows any others?

JUDY: Well you never know. Oh, David, try. Do try!

DAVID: O.K. Um . . . hold on a sec . . . um . . . yes.

[*Sings enquiringly to* GEORGE]

Rock of Ages, cleft for me?
Let me hide myself in thee? [*Pause. No response*]
Let the something and the bl-ood?

GEORGE: What yer doing?

DAVID: Oh. No.

JUDY: Oh I know! Can I try, David? Can I?

DAVID: Ra-ther. Go on.

JUDY: [*Clears throat and tries a few notes for size.* GEORGE *waits patiently*] Hummmm . . . hm.

[*Sings*]

All things bright and beautiful,
All creatures great and small . . . [*Pauses. Waits.*]

GEORGE: [*Softly*] Well, well, well, well, well.

JUDY: [*Just a shade uneasy*] Oh. [*Laughs nervously*] No good. Oh well, I expect he only knows the one.

DAVID: Yes. Well that's jolly good, George, jolly good. Well I mean it is, isn't it? When you think about it?

JUDY: Well, yes, it's staggering really.

DAVID: Yes, well. Shall we have that sherry now?

JUDY: [*Glad to be distracted*] Yes, let's. No, you sit down, love, you must be whacked.

DAVID: [*Sitting*] Well, yes, I don't mind admitting – well – it's been a strain. [JUDY *is pouring sherry*] I'm glad we've got George, though, darling.

JUDY: Mm.

DAVID: Well, it's . . . a link with Mum somehow. It's difficult to explain, but, well, it brings back a lot of memories, you know?

JUDY: [*Giving him a sherry*] Mm. Mind you don't spill.

DAVID: Oh . . . yes. Well . . . cheers, darling!

JUDY: Cheers [*They drink*]

GEORGE: How can you live on £5, eh?

JUDY: What?

GEORGE: How can you live on £5, eh? How can you live on £5, eh? [*Whistles*] £5, eh?

[*Pause*]

JUDY: Well, they've put them up now, haven't they?

DAVID: What?

JUDY: Well, the p . . . the p . . . ensions. I mean . . . They've gone up, haven't they?

DAVID: Darling, you don't seriously believe George was . . . no, that's impossible!

JUDY: Yes, of course, I'm sorry, darling. It's absurd, yes, of course.

GEORGE: How can you live on £5, eh?

[*Pause*]

DAVID: Anyway it's inflation that . . . that kills the real value of the pound . . . the pension. So that it buys less goods . . .

JUDY: Yes, and if Industrial Relations are . . .

DAVID: Inevitably some sections of the community are going to be less well off . . .

JUDY: Yes.

GEORGE: How can you live on £5, eh?

DAVID: Look, strikes cause inflation, right? And inflation means less goods in your pocket, right? Less money in the shops, right? So if you can just eradicate . . .

JUDY: . . . put a stop to . . .

DAVID: . . . strikes, there won't be any more inequalities, right?

GEORGE: Nobody comes to see me.

DAVID: Wha . . .?

GEORGE: Nobody comes to see me. Nobody comes to see me. Nobody comes to see me. [*Whistles*]

[*Pause*]

JUDY: David, I . . .

GEORGE: Ffffff [*sharp intake of breath*] It's so cold.

DAVID: Eh?

GEORGE: Fffff. It's so cold.

DAVID: Cold?

GEORGE: Fffff. So cold. So cold. So cold. So cold. [*Whistles*]

[*Pause*]

JUDY: Um . . . I don't suppose they know. I mean, they pick things up at random don't they? I mean . . . a chance remark, and they blow it up into . . . Well, it's proverbial, isn't it? 'The Thieving Magpie' . . . I mean, if, if he picked up a chance remark, well, you'd encourage him to, to, to learn it, wouldn't you? I mean you'd encourage him to . . . even though you weren't. Cold. Wouldn't you?

GEORGE: Fffffffffffff . . .
DAVID: Now look, she had a . . .
JUDY: Of course she did, darling, she had a . . .
GEORGE: Ffffff . . .
DAVID: Will you listen to me! She had a . . .
GEORGE: . . . it's so cold.
DAVID: She had a gas fire. She had it converted. She had a gas fire . . .
GEORGE: . . . It's so cold, so cold, so cold, so cold.
JUDY: [*Approaching cage resolutely*] She had a gas fire. [*No response*] She had a perfectly good gas fire. [*Waits, defying* GEORGE *to say something. Not a flicker*] She had it converted. [*Turns to go back to her chair*]
GEORGE: No shilling.
JUDY: David, I . . .
GEORGE: No shilling. No shilling. No shilling. No . . . [*Whistles*] Ffffffffff it's so cold.
DAVID: [*Pushing a peremptory finger under* GEORGE*'s beak*] All right, now that's enough!
GEORGE: [*Piteous*] Oh I've wet meself, oh I've wet meself, oh I've . . .
DAVID: [*Shaking cage violently*] Stop it! Stop it! Stop it!
GEORGE: What yer doing? [*Whistles*] What yer doing?

[*Sings enquiringly*]

Rock of Ages, cleft for me?
Let me hide myself in thee?

JUDY: I know . . . [*Rushes off*]
DAVID: Judy . . .?
GEORGE: Let the something and the bl-o-ood?
DAVID: Judy . . . ?
GEORGE: Nobody comes to see me. How can you live on £5, eh? Nobody comes to see me.

DAVID: I came . . . I tried . . . I . . .

GEORGE: £5, eh? £5, eh? [*Whistles*]

DAVID: Look, they've gone up! You get £6 now. Six whole pounds. Six!

GEORGE: Oh I've wet meself, oh I've wet meself, oh I've . . .

DAVID: [*Covering his face*] No! No!

GEORGE: . . . wet meself, oh I've [*continues till* JUDY *rushes back with a large sheet and covers the cage. They wait panting for a long time*]

JUDY: It's all right, darling, it's all right. [*Leads him to his chair and kneels in front of him*] It's all right, my love, it's all right. David? David, now look at me . . . Look at me, David.

DAVID: No, no . . .

JUDY: We'll get rid of it, we can keep the sheet on till we get rid of it . . . There, there, darling. No, don't, don't. [*She comforts him*] – And it's so unfair. I mean . . . it isn't true. It just isn't true, my darling. We . . . we couldn't have her here. We couldn't, could we? No, of course we couldn't. We discussed it, didn't we? Didn't we? And we couldn't, could we? How could we? She was so . . . so . . . so . . . wasn't she, darling? Wasn't she, my love?

DAVID: Judy . . .

GEORGE: Aaaaaaaaaaaaagh! [*They both leap up*] Aaaaaaagh!

JUDY: What . . .?

DAVID: She's fallen down the stairs.

GEORGE: Aaaaaaaaaaagh!

DAVID: Oh my God, she's fallen down the stairs.

GEORGE: [*Weakly*] Help . . . help . . . help . . . oh God please help . . . gentle Jesus . . . help . . . help . . . help . . .

DAVID: She's lying there . . .

JUDY: David . . .

DAVID: . . . at the foot of the stairs.

GEORGE: . . . help . . . help . . . help . . .

DAVID: How long?
JUDY: David . . .
DAVID: A day?
GEORGE: Nobody's coming.
DAVID: Two days?
JUDY [*Screaming*] David, stop it!
DAVID: [*Hypnotized*] Two days?
GEORGE: Nobody's coming.
DAVID: Three days?
GEORGE: [*A terrible death rattle*]
DAVID: [*Awestruck*] Three days. [*Horrified*] Three days.

[*He rips the sheet off*]

GEORGE: Well, well, well, well, well.

[*Blackout*]